Handling home care

Achieving safe, efficient and positive outcomes
for care workers and clients

HSG225

© Crown copyright 2001

First published 2001
Reprinted 2004

ISBN 0 7176 2228 2

This guidance is issued by the Health and Safety Executive.
Following the guidance is not compulsory and you are free
to take other action. But if you do follow the guidance you
will normally be doing enough to comply with the law.
Health and safety inspectors seek to secure compliance
with the law and may refer to this guidance as illustrating
good practice.

Contents

Introduction

Background

1   Manual handling (lifting, supporting, carrying, pushing and pulling by bodily force) is one of the most common activities in the home and at work. It is also one of the most common causes of strain and sprain injury and back pain. Each year an estimated 642 000 people in Great Britain suffer from a musculoskeletal disorder which affects their back and is caused by work. Around two-thirds of these people attribute their condition to manual handling activities at work. Disorders affecting the back may cost Britain up to £3 billion per year. The social and health care sector is one of the highest risk areas for workers. Almost 50% of all accidents reported each year in the social and health care sector as a whole involve manual handling, particularly assisting people with mobility.

2   There are no reliable figures for the numbers injured each year in providing care services for people in their own home, such as disabled people, the chronically sick and the elderly, but it is thought to be substantial. The result is pain; sickness absence and loss of wages for the worker; increased costs for the employer in terms of staff replacement and retraining; disruption and poor service for clients and their families. This need not be so. Most manual handling injuries are preventable. With a better approach to work organisation and job design, the risks can be eliminated or reduced.

Which activities are covered by this publication?

3   Since January 1993, the Manual Handling Operations Regulations 1992 ('the Manual Handling Regulations') have provided a general framework for tackling handling activities at work. The regulations require the following approach:
- to avoid the manual handling activities where it is reasonably practicable to do so; and, where it is not,
- to assess the risk and take appropriate steps to reduce it so far as is reasonably practicable.

4   Many workers assume that 'manual handling' refers only to lifting and carrying 'things' such as boxes, bags, sacks and other heavy loads. But manual handling not only covers these tasks. It also includes pushing and pulling trolleys or large items too heavy to lift and assisting people, particularly those with restricted mobility. Helping a disabled child out of bed or helping an elderly person go upstairs also comes within the scope of the Manual Handling Regulations. It is these kinds of 'helping people' tasks that are the particular focus of this guidance.

What about other health and safety issues?

5   This guidance does not address other health and safety issues relevant to home care situations, such as those related to infection control; use of chemicals for washing and cleaning; and gas and electrical safety.

Who is this publication aimed at?

6 The purpose of this guidance is to give practical advice on mobility to the providers of home care services. The intention is to demonstrate how others have dealt with the everyday challenges, while maintaining a quality service and minimising the risk to both the care worker and the client. The guidance focuses on physical risk to worker and client, but also takes account of the wider risks to the client of loss of independence and autonomy if they are unassisted or badly assisted. The situations described and the control measures adopted are taken from real situations. But the advice is not prescriptive. In many of the case studies, there may be further or alternative improvements that could have been made to improve the quality of care and further reduce risk. Best practice indicates a need to consult and work with the client to find effective solutions tailored to individual needs. The main significance of the advice is that it helps to highlight poor practice and contribute to the development of safer handling practices.

7 For this reason, the guidance will be particularly useful to managers of care workers and those responsible for assessing mobility assistance risk in home care situations. It will also be of interest to care workers and their representatives, and care service clients and their families.

What is the legal position?

8 The guidance does not give detailed advice on how to comply with the provisions of health and safety law. However, a brief summary of the legal framework governing employers' health and safety responsibilities in respect of home care workers' mobility and handling tasks is provided to help set the general advice and the case studies in context. More detailed advice on the regulations is available in *Manual Handling. Manual Handling Operations Regulations 1992. Guidance on Regulations* (see Appendix 2 for details).

9 Also, the guidance does not specifically address the question of how to ensure that compliance with health and safety law is compatible with other requirements under community care legislation, or the Disability Discrimination or Human Rights Acts. The guidance should be interpreted with regard to other relevant guidance, taking particular account of the need to ensure that implementation of policy and practice on lifting and handling should not place any unreasonable restrictions on client's rights to autonomy, privacy or dignity.

Is a 'no lifting' policy better than risk control?

10 Some home care service providers have now adopted so-called 'no lifting' policies in response to their duty to avoid manual handling operations. In most cases these policies in fact only require no hazardous lifting, as required by the Manual Handling Operations Regulations. But such policies can be open to misinterpretation, so that hoists are routinely prescribed for all moves and transfers irrespective of the wishes, and sometimes the needs of clients. In some cases, clients unwilling to accept such care have had the service withdrawn. These Regulations should not be applied arbitrarily to care plans in this way. It is also difficult to see how such action can be reconciled with the service providers' responsibilities under the Disability Discrimination Act and the Human Rights Act. The correct approach to this matter should start with a proper risk assessment, as described in this guidance.

11 The Regulations do not prohibit all manual handling. There needs to be a balance in approach to ensure that:

- care workers are not required to perform tasks that put them and clients at risk unreasonably;
- clients' personal wishes on mobility assistance are respected wherever possible; and
- clients' independence and autonomy is supported as fully as possible.

The co-operative approach

12 Ideally, risk assessment should be undertaken as part of a wider needs assessment process, so that health and safety issues are identified and built into the design of the care package. The assessment should be user-focused and where possible user-led, so that the individual client has choice over how needs are met and has control over her or his personal safety. In many cases, clients will have expert knowledge of their own mobility needs.

13 If used with sensitivity and due thought for the particular circumstances in each case, the way forward promoted in the regulations can provide maximum protection for both home care worker and client. A co-operative approach often works best. Some of the most innovative and effective solutions to moving and assisting situations have been found when the risk assessor, the home care worker and the client work together in partnership to consider the risks and how to tackle them.

14 In all cases the aims should be to meet the clients' expressed wishes and to meet their assessed needs for independence and autonomy, while having due regard to the safety of all concerned.

General advice

Finding the right balance

15 Providing the right type and level of care depends crucially on assessing the client's needs and making sure it is delivered in a sustainable way. It is vital, therefore, that the right balance is struck between the needs of the client and the needs of the care worker. Favouring one over the other will work to the detriment of both. User-led, user-focused assessment should produce plans that take account of lifestyle and personal preference as well as functional needs. Care that is provided either without thought for the quality of life, independence and dignity of the client or without thought for the health of the care worker is not sustainable. It creates conflict that can ultimately be costly and dangerous.

16 In view of the above, it is essential to try to ensure that any disagreements between the client and service provider are negotiated and resolved as early as possible as part of the process of assessment and care planning.

Introducing a mobility assistance policy

17 As an employer, the service provider or the employing agency has primary responsibility for ensuring the health and safety of their care workers and managing the risks associated with their work duties. In particular, mobility assistance considerations will be a significant factor in determining the overall cost of delivering any care package to the client. Health and safety risk management, therefore, must form an integral part of the care assessment, so that the hazards are identified and dealt with before the care worker and the client are put at risk.

18 One way to ensure good risk management arrangements, particularly on mobility assistance, is to have a risk management policy. The purpose of the policy will be to provide an operating framework to ensure consistency of application and compliance with legal obligations. It should set clear criteria for safe and appropriate handling and detail agreed procedures. The detail of individual policies will, of course, reflect the particular circumstances of the employer's business. In general, however, an effective and comprehensive policy would be expected to cover at least the following issues:

- how risk management fits into the overall care plan development with details of who is responsible for what and the liaison arrangements including:
  - ○ hazard identification and risk assessment procedures including the appointment of a competent person to conduct risk assessment;
  - ○ consultation procedures with staff and clients. In particular, consultation with safety representatives appointed by a recognised trade union under the Safety Representatives and Safety Committees Regulations 1977;
  - ○ arrangements for reviewing risk controls and reassessment of risk;
  - ○ encouraging staff to report problems as soon as they are recognised, for example shoulder, neck and back

pain, as it develops, so that remedial action can be taken promptly;

○ emergency arrangements;

● an established policy on how to implement risk assessment results;

● training care workers in risk management, mobility assistance and handling techniques, emergency procedures, and the appropriate use of equipment;

● supply and use of assistive devices;

● encouraging users to report problems, for example discomfort, inconvenience, as it develops, so that remedial action can be taken promptly;

● informing users of options in mobility assistance and handling techniques.

Risk management issues

Risk assessment

19 Effective risk control is based on good risk assessment. A general, or generic, risk assessment of mobility and other manual handling assistance can help to provide useful information on options for control measures. The particular circumstances of a client's home environment, however, will have considerable influence on how practical these might be. Generic risk assessment, therefore, needs to be followed up with an individual assessment of each task, conducted where the care is to be delivered.

20 The risk assessments must also address more than the obvious moving and handling problems. To be fully effective, they also need to consider how other issues, such as environmental conditions, the need for infection controls and the risk of aggressive behaviour, affect how the care is to be delivered. Risk assessment should also take account of the client's autonomy, privacy and dignity. In addition, where unpaid carers, such as family members, help with care and assistance, the unpaid carers' needs and abilities must also be taken into account. This is particularly important if the unpaid carers are expected to work alongside the care workers.

21 The most useful assessments are set out in a simple format, so that it is possible to quickly assimilate what equipment, techniques and numbers of staff are appropriate for a service user's needs. A good plan will cover both daytime and night-time care, focusing in on key moves, including:

● individual details, including identification, height and weight;

● the extent of the individual's ability to support his or her own weight and any other relevant factors, for example pain, disability, spasm, fatigue, or tendency to fall, and apprehension;

● problems with comprehension, co-operational behaviour;

● recommended methods of movement for the relevant tasks such as sitting, going to the toilet, bathing, transfers and movement in bed; details of equipment needed;

● the minimum number of staff required to help;

● other relevant risk factors.

22 There should be no blanket solutions that are routinely applied to all users.

Assessment checklist

23 It may be helpful to use a checklist during assessment as an aide-memoire. An example of a risk assessment flowchart and a general assessment checklist is provided in *Manual Handling. Manual Handling Operations Regulations 1992. Guidance on Regulations.* (see Appendix 2 for details).

Reassessment of risks

24 Situations change and to be effective, risk assessments need to be kept up to date. When procedures change or when there is reason to believe that the risk management plan may no longer be appropriate, then the risk assessment must be reviewed and if necessary a new risk management plan devised and implemented.

25 Provision should also be made, as part of the care plan, for clients to request a reassessment at any time they feel their needs or circumstances have changed.

Liaison between commissioning organisation and service provider

26 The Management of Health and Safety at Work Regulations 1999 require the commissioning organisation to pass on to the service provider any information gained during the care assessment with implications for health and safety. This must be done in time for it to feed into the preparation of the initial care plan. Without this information, the service provider will not be able to complete a suitable and

sufficient risk assessment to ensure their care workers are not exposed to unreasonable risk.

27 Where service providers consider they are unable to implement the risk management plan because of inadequate information or resources, the case needs to be referred back to the commissioning organisation for review or reassessment. This can be either when the care plan is first developed or when it is updated and altered.

More than one care provider

28 Where more than one provider delivers care to the same client, good communication and co-operation is needed between the different providers to ensure that health and safety issues such as mobility assistance are managed in a consistent manner.

Agency workers

29 In some cases, care workers may be employed by an agency and supplied to another organisation responsible for managing the provision of the care. In these circumstances, the employing agency is still responsible for the health and safety of their care worker staff. The agency, therefore, will need to liaise effectively with the care managing organisation to ensure that staff are not exposed to unreasonable risk, and that any identified risks to the client are adequately addressed.

Emergency arrangements

30 It may be necessary to arrange care at very short notice. In these emergency situations, the information made available to the care provider must be sufficiently detailed to allow the service provider to make arrangements that ensure care workers and clients are not put at risk. For example, the basic information will need to include details of:

- the client's mobility status, including ability to weight bear;
- the client's language or communication needs;
- the client's behavioural problems, if any;
- health information relevant to the assistance required (for example, if someone is hemiplegic, this is relevant to their mobility needs: the fact that they are

HIV positive is not);

- history of aggressive behaviour towards care workers by family members.

31 Where full information is not immediately available, additional precautions may need to be put in place until a full assessment can be carried out. For example, it may be necessary to arrange for two or more care workers to attend the client or to limit the nature of the care to be provided. Such arrangements, however, are only acceptable in emergency situations. They should not be considered the normal approach to managing risk.

Implementing risk assessment results

32 Sometimes the risk assessments require implementing equipment adaptions and adjustments to reduce handling risks to the care worker and/or the client. The proposed changes should be acceptable to the client and their family. This is more likely if they have been fully involved in the assessment process.

33 Though clients have no duty under health and safety law to co-operate with the service provider, and therefore cannot be coerced, prompt action must be taken to control any significant risk to the care worker identified by the risk assessment. Resistance to change is not acceptable if unsafe work practices result.

34 Although the aim should always be to find solutions acceptable to the client and their family, there will be times when this is

not immediately the case. It is essential that the service provider has procedures to ensure that unsafe work practices are minimised. Some service providers have found that a generic risk control implementation policy can help minimise difficult situations developing. These policies are developed in consultation with the client representative, to ensure that procedures for implementing the results of the risk assessments recognise the value of involving individual clients in the design of their mobility assistance plans. The generic policy defines the procedures to involve the client, their family and the care worker in the changes proposed as a result of a risk assessment and why they are necessary. This will include working with the client and their representative to find a suitable method of care which ensures the health and safety of the care worker and client, while maintaining the client's choice, dignity and independence.

35 Unless these policies have been developed in consultation with the client, there can be a danger that clients will see the policy as little more than a means of coercing them into accepting what is most convenient for the service provider.

36 Unfortunately, even where there has been involvement of the client and their family or advocates, in the assessment process, a small minority of clients are still reluctant to change their mobility assistance plans to address the risks identified. This places the service provider in a difficult situation as they have legal duties both to ensure the health and safety of the care worker and also the quality of care to the client. However, it is not acceptable under health and safety legislation that unsafe work practices, which pose immediate injury to the care worker are allowed to continue unaddressed until a satisfactory solution is found. And the service provider should have measures to manage these situations effectively.

37 A generic policy developed in consultation with the client's representatives needs to consider these infrequent situations and develop a procedure which is acceptable with the client's representatives. A policy which addresses these issues may prevent these difficulties from arising, as both the service provider and the client are fully aware of the policy and procedure from the onset and the steps to be taken if an agreement cannot be identified.

38 The main features of such policies include:

- A meeting with the client, their family and the care workers before the risk assessment to explain the risk assessment process, its aims and purpose.
- Involvement of the client and families in the risk assessment process to ensure their views and wishes regarding their care are taken into consideration.
- The results of the risk assessment are discussed with the client and the options to address the risks are fully explored with the client.
- If the client is reluctant to accept the results of the risk assessment and any changes to the care identified by the risk assessment, then the procedures defined in the policy should be implemented. Resistance to change is no excuse for allowing unsafe work practices.
- The policy developed in consultation with client representatives should clearly define the action to be taken when there is continued reluctance to accept the implementation of risk assessment. This may include several options and approaches, which need to be fully defined in the policy, with limitation of service being the final option in a hierarchy of approach.

Training care workers

39 Training is an essential component of proper risk management based on sound risk assessment. Because it is not always possible to avoid manual handling tasks even where support equipment is available, it is essential that care workers are trained in safer handling techniques.

In providing mobility assistance to an individual, however, it is not always possible to avoid manual handling tasks completely even where support equipment is available. It is essential, therefore, that all care workers who attend people with mobility difficulties are suitably trained in safer handling techniques. This training must provide the individual care worker with the knowledge and ability to recognise hazardous handling situations and determine the safe approach. Fitness of care workers needs to be addressed by the service provider in assessing the worker's capability to undertake handling tasks safely. To be effective, the training will also need to include instruction on:

- the procedures to be followed when the designated system of work cannot be applied; and
- how to secure additional assistance when it is required.

40 Such training helps to ensure that care workers can apply systems of work effectively, recognise where the agreed procedures cannot be applied, and adopt acceptable alternatives. Unless they are working alongside someone competent to instruct them, care workers should not be assigned to work which may involve transferring clients before they receive the appropriate training. But even where an individual works alongside a competent instructor, instruction and training across the whole spectrum of work undertaken should be completed before a care worker is independently assigned a case load. In some situations, the service user or their carer may have the competency to instruct the care worker on safe techniques for specific tasks. It is important that the experience and knowledge of the service user is fully considered.

Delivering training

41 Service providers have a number of options on how to deliver appropriate training to large numbers of care workers. One way is to appoint one competent person to deliver the training to each of the care workers. Where the numbers to be trained are very large, however, it may be quicker to use teams of instructors. This approach, however, will require formal arrangements to monitor the quality and consistency of the training given. Alternatively, it may be more cost effective to buy in training from a reputable training company specialising in mobility assistance and transferring clients. Whichever approach is adopted, the service provider has responsibility for ensuring the training fits in with their policy and procedures for effectively managing health and safety and is relevant and appropriate for the risks that the care workers will face in the course of their work.

Refresher training

42 Training is not a one-off event. Service providers need to ensure that care workers are kept up to date with current safe working practices and that they maintain a consistent and safe approach to assisting clients with moving and handling. Refresher training, therefore, will be required periodically. Some service providers consider that a year is a reasonable period between refresher training courses. It is for the service provider, however, to judge when it is appropriate for refresher training to take place based on their knowledge of their employees' capabilities and experience. For example, if a care worker is experiencing difficulties, they might want to provide additional training rather than wait for the next scheduled refresher course.

43 It is also vital that you continually monitor and review training procedures. Service providers should have in place monitoring procedures to highlight when training is required and also continually review the content of the training, eg how much the training relates to the job.

Supply and use of assistive devices

Assistive devices

44 It is difficult to give an authoritative description of assistive devices. In general, they are the aids to everyday living that help people to be more independent. They do not include any equipment designed to meet a nursing, medical, educational or employment need. Even so, there is a wide range of assistive devices available, including:

- manual and powered mobile hoists;
- powered ceiling track hoists;
- bathing and toileting equipment;
- small handling aids (such as slide sheets and transfer boards);
- beds and bed equipment;
- chairs, wheelchairs and chair equipment;
- walking and standing aids.

45 A number of the case studies in this publication demonstrate how such equipment may be used to assist mobility and reduce risk.

Supply of equipment

46 Since April 1993, there have been community care policies which require an assessment of need and, where necessary, co-ordination of packages of care to enable elderly and disabled people to remain in their own home. The delivery of the agreed care package, however, can be by statutory services, by contracted voluntary services or by commercial services, or by means of direct payments made to the client in lieu of services. In most cases, however, it is the statutory services that will supply any equipment identified in the care package as necessary to secure the appropriate quality of care and reduce the risks to both client and care worker.

Standard equipment

47 Not everyone's needs will be met by standard equipment. The client's physical and general health condition, living environment and lifestyle must be considered, when assessing the suitability of particular items of equipment such as beds, chairs, mobile hoist and slings, etc to ensure appropriateness. For instance, it is dangerous to use handling equipment outside its recommended weight limits. There will be occasions, therefore, when it may be necessary to adapt or make special alterations to the standard equipment. Such adaptations should only be undertaken in conjunction with the manufacturer's advice.

Use of equipment

48 Clients and care workers can be injured if equipment, even the right equipment, is used inappropriately or is not properly maintained. Service providers, or employing agencies, must ensure, therefore, that equipment is in good working order, and that all care workers are aware of and understand the appropriate application and limitations of the different pieces of equipment they are expected to use.

Equipment training

49 One way to ensure that care workers are competent to use mobility assistance equipment, is to expand handling techniques training to include instruction on:

● the different types of equipment available, and the appropriate use of each;

● the safe use of hoists and their slings;

● the recharging of electric hoists;

● the safe use of the smaller aids, such as handling belts, transfer boards, rotundas;

● the identification of possible faults and the necessary safety checks that should be made each time before use;

● the procedures to follow when equipment is damaged and unsafe to use, or if it fails during use.

Choice of equipment

50 Clients should be given full information on the range of equipment available and offered choices on the equipment to be chosen. Client's opinions on whether the equipment will meet their needs should be sought and respected. Where a client does not want a particular piece of equipment, because it does not suit her or his lifestyle, efforts should be made to find alternative solutions. For example, a person may reject the offer of a hospital bed, because they wish to continue to use a double bed. Alternatives might include bed blocks to raise the height permanently or an electric mattress variator to raise the height as required.

51 Where non-standard equipment is supplied or adaptations are made to standard equipment in order to meet the particular needs of a client, the care worker's training may need to be reinforced with more specific instruction and practice at the client's home. If the care workers are expected to use the equipment alongside other care providers, it may also be appropriate to arrange for the others to take part in this specific training. It is highly desirable for the client to be fully involved.

Written instructions

52 To help avoid confusion when using the equipment, especially hoists and slings, it might be helpful to produce written instructions supported with photographs or drawings. These instructions can then be incorporated into the care plan for future reference by anyone providing care to the client. But special arrangements would have to be made for care workers or carers who cannot read English. In some cases, alternative formats, such as large print or audio format, might be required.

Responsibility for maintaining equipment

53 Assistive devices must be adequately maintained to ensure that they continue to be suitable and safe for use. The responsibility for maintenance generally lies with the care worker's employer:

● *Equipment provided by the service provider to reduce risk to the care worker.* If the service provider supplies equipment such as a stair lift, bath lift or toilet riser, primarily to reduce the risk of injury to care workers while attending to the client, then the equipment may be considered work equipment. In these circumstances, the Provision and Use of Work Equipment Regulations 1998 (PUWER) will apply. Depending on the type of equipment, the Lifting Operation and Lifting Equipment Regulations 1998 (LOLER) may also apply. These regulations require the equipment provider to maintain and inspect the equipment;

● *Equipment provided by the service provider to assist the client's mobility.* If the equipment is mainly for the client's own use, then the PUWER/LOLER regulations will not apply. However, the equipment provider has responsibility under the general provisions of the Health and Safety at Work etc Act 1974, to ensure that it is safe for the client and care workers to use. Though the PUWER/LOLER regulations may not apply, their provisions can be used as a guide to establish proper maintenance arrangements;

● *Equipment provided by the client.* Clients have no duties under health and safety legislation to maintain their own equipment even if care workers use it while providing care assistance. Nor do service providers have power under any circumstances to compel clients to have their own equipment maintained. As an employer, however, the service provider is still responsible for ensuring their care workers' safety. It is up to the service provider, therefore, to assess whether any equipment provided by the client is suitable for their care workers to use, and also to discuss with the client any changes, which might need to be considered.

Assessing clients' equipment

54 In some cases, clients may have a service agreement with the equipment supplier, particularly for major items of equipment, such as a stair lift or mobile hoist. Where these arrangements provide evidence that the equipment is properly maintained and the service provider is satisfied that it is safe for their care workers to use, then it can be incorporated into the care delivery plan. It will be necessary, however, to confirm periodically that the service contract continues to operate and the necessary checks have been carried out regularly. In the absence of such service agreements, the service provider will need to take other measures to ensure the safety of their care workers. This may be by taking over, with the client's agreement, the equipment maintenance arrangements or instructing the care workers not to use the equipment.

Case studies on mobility and risk control

General information

Each case study is set out in a standard format as below:

- Task
- Manual handling problem
- Control measures
- *Costs
- Benefits
- Additional comments/suggestions

*HSE accepts no responsibility for the accuracy of the costs of the assistive devices mentioned in this guidance.

Case studies' structure

For ease of reference, the case studies are grouped according to type of situation. Each group has a short general introduction.

- Assisting into and out of bed and changing position in bed
  (Case studies 1–8);

- Assisting into and out of the bath
  (Case studies 9–10);

- Using the toilet
  (Case studies 11–17);

- Moving around the house
  (Case studies 18–23);

- Managing the stairs
  (Case study 24);

- Assisting into and out of the car
  (Case studies 25–27).

Assisting into and out of bed and changing position in bed

Handling task

Helping a client into and out of bed.

Hazards

Hazards can arise from a number of different things. Some of the common ones are: the height of the bed, the width of the bed, the position of the bed, particularly with low divans; mattress condition; confined space in the bedroom; unpredictable client behaviour; clients with limited ability to support their own weight; care workers assisting a client in an uncoordinated manner, clothing which restricts the care worker's movements.

Risks

Some of the main risks will be to both the care worker and the client:

- The care worker is at risk of back and neck injury from the need to adopt awkward postures (stooping, bending, and twisting) while supporting the weight of the client and assisting the client up into the standing or lowering to the sitting position; from manoeuvring the client into the middle of the bed and helping them into a sitting position; from trying to take sudden remedial action when a client is unable to support their own weight and starts to fall.

- The client is at risk of musculoskeletal disorder and tissue injury from inappropriate systems of assisting up into the sitting or standing position or lowering to the sitting position; of bruising or worse from falling.

Control measures

The risks can be avoided or minimised in a number of ways, eg a more appropriately designed bed; handling aids; repositioning of furniture etc, depending on the particular circumstances. Careful planning of positioning can reduce the need for additional handling. Case studies 1-8 demonstrate how others have tackled these challenges.

Using bed rails to help a client roll over

Task

Mr G had multiple sclerosis and was cared for by two care workers. He had full use of his hands and arms but little strength in his legs and feet. Mr G weighed about 12 stone/75 kg.

Manual handling problem

The care workers washed Mr G while he was still in bed. One care worker would roll Mr G towards her and hold him in that position while a second care worker washed his back. The holding task was uncomfortable for the care worker and caused lower back pain. An occupational therapist reviewed the risk assessment and identified a manual handling risk from supporting Mr G's weight in a static posture.

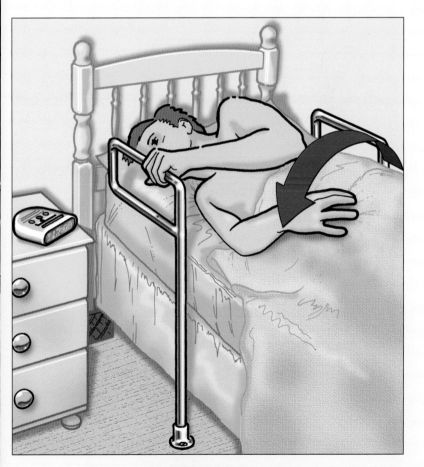

Control measures

To make best use of Mr G's arm strength, bed rails were installed, which were screwed to the floor on each side near the top of the bed. This allowed Mr G to reach across with his opposite arm and use the rails to roll and support himself in the right position.

The occupational therapist also provided refresher training to the care workers on their handling techniques for supporting a client.

Cost

The cost of the alterations included £70 for each of the bed rails and a further £40 for fitting.

Benefits

The rails reduced the manual handling risk to both care workers during the washing and dressing tasks.

Using the strength in his arms helped Mr G maintain his mobility and made him feel less dependent. He liked the feeling that he could assist the care workers.

Additional suggestions/comments

Where there is a delay in fitting the hand rails, the handling risk can be reduced when rolling and supporting a client in bed if the care worker puts their knee on the bed to help maintain the curve of their spine.

Using handrails to help a client transfer between bed/wheelchair/armchair/mobile commode

Task

Mr J had experienced a stroke which caused a weakness on his right side. He was unstable on his feet and needed assistance with his personal care. He was reluctant to use his unaffected side as this caused him discomfort. He weighed about 10 stone/65 kg. Two care workers visited on a daily basis.

Manual handling problem

The care workers assisted Mr J with all transfers between bed, wheelchair, armchair and mobile commode and supported him during washing and dressing. The transfers involved helping Mr J into a standing position.

For example, to transfer from bed to armchair, Mr J moved himself into a sitting position on the edge of the bed, the two care workers stood in front of him, then stooped, each placing one arm under one of Mr J's arms and pulled him into an upright position. They then supported his weight, one on each side, while Mr J moved his feet and turned. They then lowered him into the chair.

A similar technique was used to help Mr J transfer from armchair to wheelchair/mobile commode and to raise him while the care workers assisted him with washing and dressing etc.

The care workers reported that they were having difficulties with the transfers. A risk assessment identified that they were at risk of

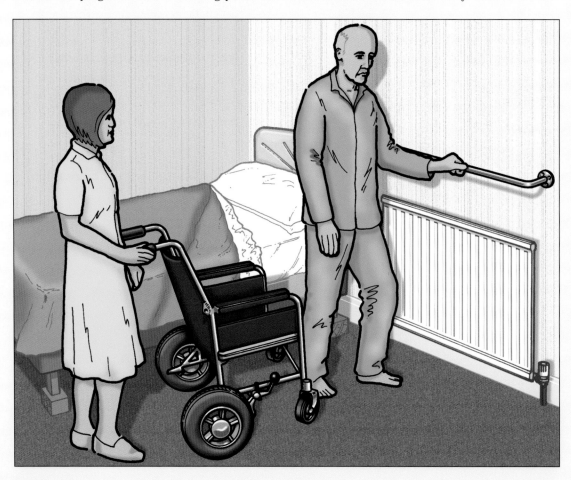

injury while assisting Mr J to stand and supporting him while he stood. One of the problems was that Mr J's bed was low in relation to the height of the wheelchair.

Control measures

The bed was raised on bed raisers to the same height as the wheelchair and a handrail was installed. This enabled Mr J to pull himself up into a standing position. He could then steady and support himself for dressing and washing. The handrail also enabled Mr J to lower himself, which was useful when transferring between wheelchair, armchair and mobile commode.

Cost

The cost of the alterations included £15 for the supply and installation of the handrail and £16 for the bed raisers.

Benefits

The new procedures reduced the manual handling risk to the care workers. With the help of the handrail, Mr J was able to stand and manage the transfers without any assistance from the care workers. While he supported himself on the handrail, the care workers could exchange the wheelchair/armchair/chair behind him and this reduced the number of transfers needed. The handrail also encouraged Mr J to use his unaffected side.

Raising the bed to the same height as the wheelchair reduced the distance Mr J had to reach when transferring between the bed and his chair.

Additional suggestions/comments

If Mr J had not been able to pull himself up from the bed into a standing position, the risk to the care workers could have been reduced with the use of a padded non-slip handling belt fitted around Mr J's waist. Both care workers would need to sit either side on the bed holding the handling belt end loops and assist the standing procedure co-ordinating their actions with the command of 'Ready, Steady, Stand'. The cost of a large padded non-slip belt is around £25.

An armchair fitted with brake castors would help for repositioning once the person is sitting in it. A grab rail positioned on a wall close to the armchair would allow transfer from wheelchair to armchair.

It might be useful to position a zimmer in front of a client with poor standing balance to provide them with some extra support. This frees the care workers to wash and dress the lower half of a client without having to simultaneously support them.

Using a slide sheet to assist with bed transfers

Task

Mr B had experienced a stroke which had affected movement on his left side. He was tall and weighed about 13 stone/85 kg. He needed assistance with all transfers and his wife was the sole carer. He visited a day care centre 2–3 times a week to give his wife respite.

Manual handling problem

Mr B was able to use a rotunda (turntable with a frame) with only minimal assistance for most transfers. However, Mrs B found helping her husband back into bed particularly difficult and physically demanding. The rotunda helped Mr B to manage the transfer and sit on the edge of the bed; his wife then placed one arm behind his shoulders, stooped down, put her other arm around his lower legs and lifted his legs onto the bed. Once Mr B was on the bed, his wife pushed him into the middle and then pulled him up the bed to get him into a comfortable position.

The occupational therapist reassessed the task and identified manual handling risks to the carer from stooping while lifting Mr B's legs and also from pushing and pulling him up the bed.

Control measures

Two slide sheets and a handling sling were supplied to help reduce the need for strenuous handling. One slide sheet was placed on the bed for Mr B to sit on when he used the rotunda. The other slide sheet was placed where Mr B's shoulders would rest when lying down. The handling sling was put around his ankles to help lift his legs and rotate Mr B into bed. With training in the use of the slide sheets and handling sling, Mrs B was able to help her husband into bed more easily. She put one hand behind his shoulders and holding the handling sling in the other, Mrs B turned her husband onto the bed. As Mr B turned, the slide sheet moved him to the centre. With the second slide sheet under Mr B's shoulders, Mrs B could help move him up

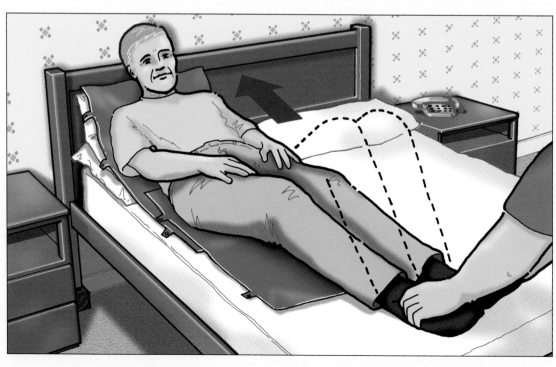

the bed by bending his knees and holding onto his feet while he used his own strength to push himself up the bed. Mrs B then removed the slide sheets easily by pulling them out in an upward direction. This also helped position Mr B on the bed.

Cost

The slide sheets cost £10 each and the handling sling £25.

Benefits

The handling aids reduced the handling risks to Mrs B:

- The handling sling removed the need for Mrs B to stoop; she was able to remain in an upright position when lifting her husband's legs on to the bed;
- The slide sheets reduced friction and helped Mr B to slide, turn and move up the bed with minimal assistance from his wife.

Additional suggestions/comments

An alternative solution to assist repositioning in bed would have been to fit a wall mounted handrail at the top of the bed. This would have let Mr B use the strength in his unaffected side to pull himself up the bed.

Slide sheets and handling slings are cheap and can be used in a wide variety of situations to help reduce manual handling risks. If no handling sling is available, a towel could be used. Provided carers are properly trained, therefore, it can be helpful to give them routine access to such equipment.

Helping a client out of bed

Task

Mrs W had arthritis. Her joints were very stiff in the mornings and she became very tired with shortness of breath in the evenings. She weighed about 12 stone/75 kg. Mrs W needed the help of two care workers to get in and out of bed.

Manual handling problem

When helping Mrs W out of bed, the care workers used a drag lift to bring her from a lying to a sitting position. One care worker then supported her weight while the other reached over, stooped down, twisted round and lifted Mrs W's legs over the side of the bed. Both then assisted Mrs W to stand. Because the bed was a low divan, both care workers had to stoop during the task. The procedures were reversed when Mrs W went to bed. In the evening, however, Mrs W was generally very short of breath and, although keen to assist, she was unable to help in any way. A drag lift was used to lift her up the bed.

After taking part in a client handling training course, the care workers realised that their handling techniques were unsafe for both themselves and Mrs W. They asked the local back care advisor to reassess the task.

Control measures

An electrical mattress variator was provided to assist Mrs W to sit forward in the bed and to lower her from sitting to lying. In the mornings, a flexible turning disc was used under her bottom and a slide sheet under her feet to enable one care worker to assist her to swivel herself round and sit on the edge of the bed. The height of her bed was raised using bed raisers to eliminate the need for the care

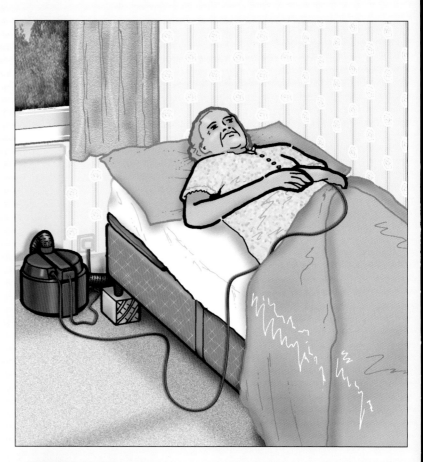

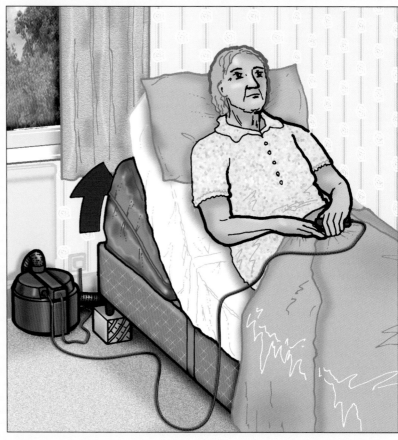

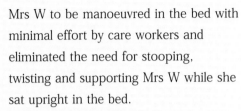

workers to stoop while helping Mrs W up. In the evenings, a mobile hoist was used to transfer Mrs W from her chair to her bed.

Cost

The cost of the electrical mattress variator was about £400; the mobile hoist cost £700, the flexible turn disc £50, and the small slide sheet £10.

Benefits

Both care workers and Mrs W were happy with the solution:

- The electrical mattress variator removed the need for a drag lift which was unsafe for the care workers and for Mrs W.
- The turning disc and slide sheet enabled

Mrs W to be manoeuvred in the bed with minimal effort by care workers and eliminated the need for stooping, twisting and supporting Mrs W while she sat upright in the bed.

- Adjusting the bed height reduced the need for the care workers to stoop. It also reduced the effort needed by Mrs W to stand.
- Mrs W was pleased that the new procedures helped her retain as much independence as possible.

Additional suggestions/comments

If there is a delay in providing the hoist, the flexible turning disc and sliding sheet could be used to reduce risk in the interim, when helping to put Mrs W to bed. As an alternative to the turning disc, a slide sheet under her bottom could be used.

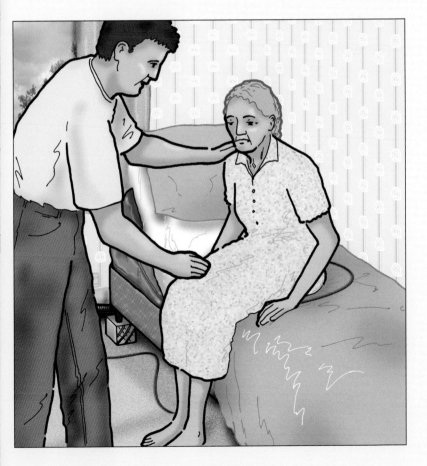

Using a ceiling track hoist to assist a client with transfers

Task

Miss J had severe multiple sclerosis. She lived with her parents and the house had been adapted for her needs. She needed help with transfers between her bed and her wheelchair. She was cared for by her parents and employed a care worker via an agency to visit each weekday.

Manual handling problem

Miss J had a mobile hoist in the bedroom, but it was difficult to use because the amount of furniture left little manoeuvring space. As a result, her carers and the care worker needed to adopt awkward postures in order to hoist her. They also kept bumping into the furniture. Miss J herself was at risk of injury from bumping into furniture when hoisted. Miss J was concerned about the risk of injury to her parents, care worker and herself. She recognised that the hoist was difficult to move on the carpeted floor, requiring strenuous pushing and pulling by two people. Between Miss J, her carers and care worker, they decided to replace the carpet with linoleum, but this change of surface did not completely resolve the problem. Miss J decided to seek

professional advice from the occupational therapist. The occupational therapist carried out a risk assessment for Miss J in consultation with herself, her parents, her care worker and the care worker's agency.

Control measures

Miss J needed all the furniture in her room to receive visitors. None of it, therefore, could be removed to increase manoeuvring space. For this reason, the occupational therapist recommended a ceiling track hoist be installed to allow Miss J to be hoisted into and out of bed.

Benefits

A ceiling track hoist reduced the risk to the carers and care worker from pushing and pulling the hoist. It also eliminated the risk of injury to everyone from bumping into furniture. Because the hoist needed less

physical effort, the carers and care worker found it easier to use. It also gave them greater control of Miss J's movements while she was in the sling. The task took less time to perform and it reduced the number of people required to hoist Miss J. The extra floor space allowed Miss J's wheelchair to be stored in the bedroom, instead of in the hallway where it had been an obstruction.

Miss J was happy with the solution because the hoist allowed a smoother transfer and reduced risk of injury to Miss J, her carers and care worker.

Cost

The cost of the ceiling track hoist was £1755.

Additional suggestions/comments

The restricted space available in Miss J's bedroom should have highlighted the need for an overhead hoist. The appropriateness of the original risk assessment that recommended a mobile hoist must be questioned.

When recommending a ceiling track hoist, it is advisable to consult a housing advisor to ensure that the roof joists are strong enough and in the correct position to attach a hoist and the additional weight of the person.

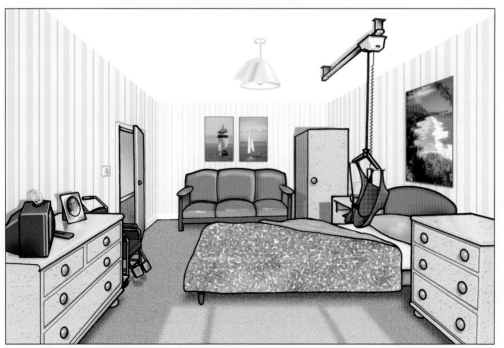

Using a mobile hoist for all transfers

Task

Mrs J had had two hip replacements. She had a lot of pain in her hips and knees. She could not walk and needed help transferring between her bed and chair/commode. She was assisted by her husband and one care worker, who visited four times a day.

Manual handling problem

A standing hoist (stand aid) helped with the transfers but it could only be used to lift or lower Mrs J when she was sitting on the edge of her bed or chair. Her husband and the care worker helped her sit up in bed and then turned her round into the right position for the hoist. Mr J then supported his wife from behind and the care worker held her from the front to prevent her slipping off the bed. While supporting her, the care worker pulled the standing hoist into position and put the sling round Mrs J. The procedure was reversed to put Mrs J to bed. She was then moved into a lying position and pulled up the bed to make her comfortable. Mrs J experienced pain under her arms and in her back from the standing hoist sling and when being moved into position on the bed.

An occupational therapist visited the home and identified the high manual handling risk to Mrs J, her husband and the care worker from the strenuous pulling to reposition Mrs J in bed and also supporting her full weight while reaching for other equipment. The occupational therapist also considered the standing hoist unsafe because Mrs J's knees rotated externally and she was unable to put one of them on the knee plate. This put all her weight on one foot which made her unstable and caused her pain.

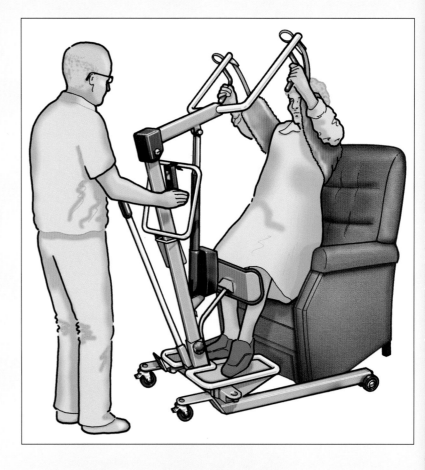

Control measures

The occupational therapist recommended replacing the standing hoist with an electric mobile hoist. A sling was chosen so that Mrs J could be hoisted in a lying position to help reduce the weight taken through her painful hips. The electric hoist was needed because neither the carer nor the care worker were particularly tall and would have found it difficult to use a hoist with a wind handle on a tall mast. The furniture in the house was rearranged and loose mats removed from the floors to give a clear and even floor surface for using the hoist in the lounge, bedroom and hallway. Training in how to use the hoist was provided for the carer and care worker.

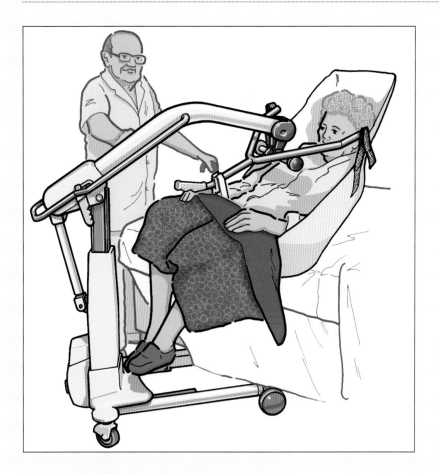

Cost

The hoist and slings cost approximately £2500.

Benefits

The mobile hoist allowed Mrs J to be positioned safely in the bed and hoisted from a reclined position. This eliminated the need for strenuous pushing/pulling/holding in awkward postures and reduced the risk of manual handling injury to both carer and care worker. The time taken to perform the task was reduced and only one carer was needed twice a day.

Mrs J was happy with the new transfer procedures because the reclining position reduced the pressure on her hips and was less painful. Mr J was happy that he had more scope to take care of his wife by himself.

Additional suggestions/comments

The occupational therapist's assessment that it was unsafe for Mrs J to use the stand aid meant that Mrs J would have required bed care until the mobile hoist arrived. Alternatively, a temporary increase of care workers to assist in manually transferring her from her bed could be considered.

Using a free-standing hoist to transfer from bed to chair

Task

Mrs V had recently been in hospital. Since returning home, her mobility had deteriorated and she could no longer get about with only her walking stick. In particular, she needed help with transfers between her bed (a hospital bed) and the chair provided as an aid to rehabilitation. Her husband was her carer, but two care workers visited three times a day to assist with washing, dressing and personal care. A mobile hoist was used to lift and lower Mrs V in bed but her bedroom was very small and this made the hoist difficult to use.

Manual handling problem

The occupational therapist reviewed the situation and decided that the mobile hoist was unsuitable. Excessive pushing and pulling was needed to get the hoist into position and the operators had to adopt awkward postures when using it. The confined space made it difficult to move the mobile hoist safely into the bedroom from the hall, where it was normally kept. In addition, the design of the hospital bed meant that the hoist could not be positioned as close to the bed as it should be. It was also very easy to jam the hoist underneath the bed and this required strenuous pulling to get it free. The hoist was also an obstruction stored in the hall.

Control measures

The occupational therapy manager recommended replacing the mobile hoist with a bedhead hoist; this is a free-standing hoist with stabilising legs positioned against the wall at the head of the bed. The hoist company representative was invited to set up the hoist so that Mrs V and her husband could try it out and test its suitability. The demonstration confirmed that the hoist could work well in the confined space. For the transfers, the sling could be fitted around Mrs V in bed and then attached to the spreader bar. Mrs V could then use the controls to raise herself. The care workers guide her over to the chair so that she could lower herself onto it. With experience, Mrs V decided that it was better to keep the sling on all day so that she could be lifted quickly and easily during the day. A sheepskin lined sling, which was more comfortable to sit on, was ordered. In the interim, Mrs V used two padded leg wraps, that friends had made for her. These helped protect her upper legs when using the hoist.

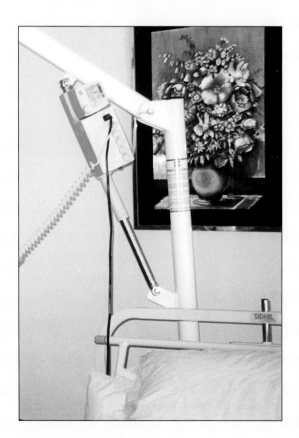

Cost

The hoist and slings cost approximately £1100.

Benefits

The hoist reduced the manual handling risk to the carer and the care workers; it removed the need for strenuous pushing and pulling to get the hoist into position, and the awkward postures during use.

Mrs V was happy to be able to control her movement in the hoist and was pleased with the smooth movement. She had not liked the swinging and jolting she experienced with the mobile hoist. She was also able to move between the bed and the chair when she wanted and did not have to wait for a care worker to transfer her.

Mr V was happy because he could use the bedhead hoist by himself. The care workers still visited in the morning to wash Mrs V and put her in the chair, but he was then able to care for his wife for the rest of the day. This gave him hope of being progressively able to look after his wife on his own.

The hall was now clear of obstruction.

Additional suggestions/comments

As an alternative, a gantry hoist can be used instead of a bedhead hoist, particularly for heavy clients who exceed the weight limit for most mobile hoists. A gantry hoist costs approximately £4000. Keeping a sling on all day may not always be practical. An alternative would be to offer a well-designed sling made from an appropriate material which can usually be easily removed and refitted by a well-trained care worker. The introduction of slings lined with low friction materials similar to those used in sliding sheets etc have made this even easier.

Using an angled transfer board to transfer from bed to chair

Task

Mr F had multiple sclerosis and needed help with transfers between his bed, chair and commode. He was cared for at home by two district nurses, but they were finding the transfers increasingly difficult. The room was small and unsuitable for a mobile hoist.

Manual handling problem

Mr F's ability to stand and weight bear varied. Fortunately, he was aware of his capabilities and he was able to advise the nurses each day whether he was able to support his weight. On these days, the nurses managed the standing and transfers with the aid of a transfer belt. On the other days, however, he was unable to stand and his legs were liable to give way during the transfers. To help deal with this situation, and with Mr F's agreement, an overhead tracking hoist was recommended. But this could not be installed immediately. The nurses, therefore, requested further advice from the back care advisor about what could be done in the interim period.

Control measures

The back care advisor recommended that the nurses continue to transfer Mr F with the transfer belt on the days when he was capable of supporting his own weight. On the other days, when he was not able to weight bear, the recommendation was to use an angled transfer board. For this, Mr F was rolled onto his side at the edge of the bed and his feet lifted onto the floor. He then pushed himself into a sitting position over the edge of the bed. The transfer belt was put on and the angled transfer board positioned to bridge the

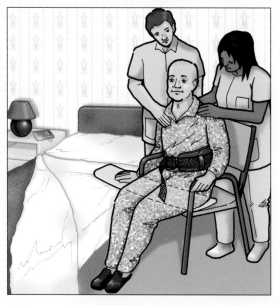

gap between the bed and chair/commode. Using the transfer belt the nurses helped Mr F slide along the transfer board and onto the chair/commode.

Cost

The cost of the angled transfer board was about £40 and the transfer belt about £25.

Benefits

This interim solution enabled Mr F to continue to use the commode and to sit out of bed. The alternative would have been to nurse him in bed.

Additional suggestions/comments

The level of the bed and chair/commode must be at a similar height to use the transfer board safely. Bed raisers can be used to overcome the problem of low beds. Another potential problem is that very soft mattresses can compress and reduce the height of the bed. This needs to be considered when assessing the suitability of a transfer board. Transfer boards should be available to care workers and nursing staff as 'stock items'.

Assisting into and out of the bath

Handling task

Helping a client to get into and out of the bath.

Hazards

Hazards can arise, for example, from the height and depth of the bath; baths positioned against the wall; confined space in the bathroom; unpredictable client behaviour; clients with limited ability to support their own weight; or uncoordinated lifting assistance for care workers.

Risks

The risk will be to both the care worker and the client:

- The care worker is at risk of back and neck injury from the need to stoop to assist the client's feet over the side of the bath; to adopt awkward postures (stooping, bending, and twisting) to get the client into the bath and then lower or raise them while in the bath; and from trying to take sudden remedial action when a client is unable to support their own weight and starts to fall.
- The client is at risk of shoulder injury from assisting up into the standing position or lowering to the sitting position; of bruising or worse from falling.

Control measures

The risks can be avoided or minimised in a number of ways, eg handling aids etc, depending on the particular circumstances. Case studies 9-10 demonstrate how others have tackled these challenges.

Using a bath seat to help a client into and out of the bath

Task

Mrs B weighed around 8 stone/50 kg. She had Parkinson's disease and needed help getting into and out of the bath. For religious reasons, Mrs B did not bathe by immersion; she poured water over herself from a bucket. A care worker visited her daily to help.

Manual handling problem

Mrs B could get herself into the bath without assistance, but it was deep and she needed help to get down to a sitting position. To do this, the care worker supported some of her weight, while leaning over the bath in a bent posture. To help Mrs B get out of the bath, the care worker bent over and braced herself against the side of the bath and offered Mrs B her arm. Mrs B then grasped hold of the care worker's arm and pulled herself up. The care worker was concerned about the risk to both herself and Mrs B from this task. She informed the home care co-ordinator who visited the home to review the risk assessment.

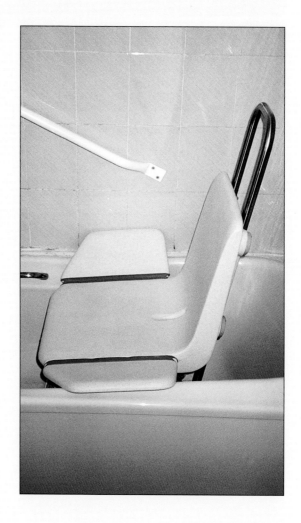

Control measures

The home care co-ordinator identified the manual handling risk from the awkward handling postures. Following discussions with the occupational therapy department, a bath board was installed. This was a board placed across the bath so that the seat was level with the top of the bath. With the bath board in place, Mrs B was able to sit on the seat and the care worker could swing her legs into the bath. For religious reasons Mrs B only needed to pour water over herself, she did not need to lower herself down from the board into the bath. When the bathing was finished, the care worker would swing Mrs B's legs onto the floor and Mrs B would stand up. As Mrs B's condition worsened there was a fear that she could fall off the bath board. To prevent this a bath chair was provided which had a back support and was contoured to the shape of the body.

Cost

The bath board cost approximately £30 and the bath chair cost approximately £600.

Benefits

The bath board and chair reduced the manual handling risk to the care worker because she no longer had to adopt awkward postures and support Mrs B's weight.

The risk of injury to Mrs B from slipping while getting down into the bath and up out of the bath was avoided. Because she needed less assistance with bathing, she was also able to maintain more of her independence.

The bath seat and chair were light and could be easily moved out of the bath, so other family members could use the bath normally.

Additional suggestions/comments

Although this would be more expensive, an alternative to the bath chair would be to install a shower system.

Helping a client into and out of a bath

Task

Mrs L weighed around 9 stone/55 kg. She was physically frail, and had had two hip replacements which left her with poor balance. She lived with her blind husband in a ground floor flat. Mrs L wanted to have a bath but could no longer get in and out of the bath safely. She contacted her local Social Services department and requested a home care service.

Manual handling problem

The care worker supervisor and a care worker visited Mrs L's home to assess her functional capabilities and the care requirements. During the visit the care worker supervisor assessed the potential risk to the client and care workers during the bathing task. Mrs L was unsteady on her feet and could not step into or out of the bath by herself. If care workers were to assist her with bathing, they would need to support her weight or assist her to get her out of the bath. This would involve handling in a twisted and stooped posture.

Control measures

As a temporary measure with Mrs L's agreement, it was arranged that a care worker would visit Mrs L once a week with a portable bath chair. A trolley was provided so that the care worker could transport the chair and the small compressor needed to operate it. Once in Mrs L's home the chair was set up in the bath and raised. Mrs L would sit on the board attached to the chair and slide onto it. The care worker would then raise her legs into the bath and Mrs L would press the controls and lower herself and the chair into the bath. She was then able to wash herself unaided. For a more long-term solution, the occupational therapist recommended a permanent, battery-

operated, chair. This chair was similar to the compressor-operated chair, but eliminated the hazard from the trailing flex since there was no need to connect it to the electricity supply.

Cost

The cost of the portable chair was approximately £460 and the permanent chair was approximately £800.

Benefits

The chair eliminated the manual handling risk to the care worker and the care worker was happy not to have to bring the chair each time she visited.

Mrs L was satisfied with the solution because she could continue to bathe independently and retain her dignity. She could cover herself with a towel as she was helped onto the chair and could have privacy while washing.

Instructions of how to bath Mrs L were contained in her file at her home and a copy kept at the office. With the chair permanently in place, family members could also help Mrs L to bath more frequently.

Mrs L had occasional dizzy spells and the bath chair was also useful in helping to raise her from the floor after a fall.

Additional suggestions/comments

As an alternative, showering facilities would also eliminate the need for getting in and out of the bath.

Using the toilet

Handling task

Helping a client to get onto and off the toilet.

Hazards

Hazards can arise from the height of the toilet; confined space in the lavatory; unpredictable client behaviour; clients with limited ability to support their own weight; and uncoordinated lifting assistance for care workers.

Risks

The risk will be to both the care worker and the client:

- The care worker is at risk of back and neck injury from the need to adopt awkward postures (stooping, bending, and twisting) and assisting the client up into the standing or lowering to the sitting position, working in often cramped conditions with fixed furniture; from trying to take sudden remedial action when a client is unable to support their own weight and starts to fall.

- The client is at risk of shoulder injury from being pulled up into the standing position or lowered to the sitting position; of bruising or worse from falling.

- Fixed furniture, eg sinks are not suitable for supporting weight, and may collapse under use.

Control measures

The risks can be avoided or minimised in a number of ways, eg adaptations to the toilet; handling aids etc, depending on the particular circumstances. Case studies 11-17 demonstrate how others have tackled these challenges.

Using an adapted rotunda to help a client onto the commode

Task

Mrs S had rheumatoid arthritis. She had rheumatoid nodules on her forearms, painful joints and limited movement in her left knee. Her right leg had been amputated above the knee. Two care workers visited her four times a day to help her transfer between her bed and a mobile commode. They also washed her in bed and assisted her in dressing. Her husband helped her with a bedpan between home care visits.

Manual handling problem

To transfer to the commode, Mrs S would sit herself up with assistance of an electrically operated 'profiling' bed which raised the head of the mattress. She could then turn and

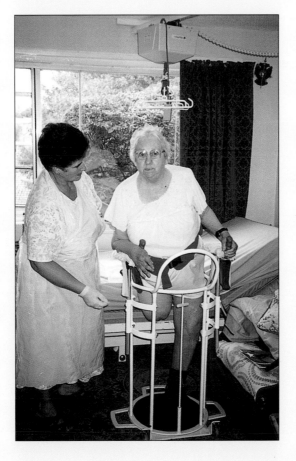

position her legs over the edge of the bed. The commode was placed at 90° to the bed and a turntable was positioned on the floor. The two care workers stood either side of Mrs S, stooped and each linked one of their arms under her arms. They then assisted Mrs S to a standing position on the turntable and supported her as she was turned around so that she could be lowered onto the commode. While supporting Mrs S on the turntable, both care workers had to adopt awkward postures. One care worker had to stretch over the commode and assist Mrs S in a stooped posture. The second care worker was forced to twist and lean because the bed impeded her movement when Mrs S was on the turntable. The care workers suffered from back pain which they felt was work-related and told their manager about the transfer problems. An occupational therapist visited the home with a health and safety training officer to assess the risks. They identified risk of injury to the care workers from handling Mrs S in twisted and stooped postures. There was also a severe risk of injury/discomfort to Mrs S from being handled under the arms.

Control measures

The risk assessment found that the care workers were not aware that the height of the bed could be adjusted to help prevent the need for stooping to assist Mrs S into a standing position. The care workers, therefore, were trained in how the various features of the bed could be used to assist with Mrs S's care.

In view of Mrs S's arm strength, the occupational therapist recommended a rotunda (turntable with a pulpit frame), to help Mrs S stand by herself, and a handling belt for the transfer to the commode. The alternative was to use a hoist. Mrs S preferred not to use the hoist because she was going to be fitted with an artificial limb and wanted to maintain her weight-bearing ability. The rotunda was purchased, but because the pain in her forearms made it difficult for Mrs S to hold or lean on the frame, it needed to be adapted. A small gutter covered with sheepskin was placed on both sides of the top rail. In this way, Mrs S could lean her forearms into the gutter, with minimal discomfort, and did not have to rely on gripping the frame.

With the revised procedure for transferring to the commode, Mrs S sat up in bed and turned herself round in the usual way. The care workers then positioned the rotunda in front of Mrs S and raised the bed to the highest level; this made it easier for Mrs S to pull herself to the standing position. She was then able to transfer herself from the bed to the rotunda without assistance. The care workers moved the mobile commode into position and turned the rotunda, to position Mrs S in front of the commode. Mrs S then lowered herself onto the commode.

To transfer back to the bed, the process was reversed. The commode, however, was low and to help Mrs S up, the care workers placed a handling belt around Mrs S to offer her minimal assistance as she pulled herself up from the commode to the rotunda.

The continuing problem with the low commode was also recognised. The occupational therapist has continued to explore ways to raise the mobile commode so that Mrs S can transfer from the commode to the rotunda without the assistance of the care workers.

Cost

The cost was £400 for the adapted rotunda and approximately £25 for the handling belt.

Benefits

The rotunda reduced the amount of handling in the transfer to the commode. In particular, it reduced the care workers exposure to manual handling risk from stretching and lifting in a bent and twisted posture. It also eliminated the need for the drag lift and reduced the risk of injury to Mrs S.

The wishes of the client were met, as a hoist was not essential and Mrs S could, therefore, continue to weight bear as part of the transfer process. This was physically and psychologically important for her continued rehabilitation and future use of the artificial limb.

Additional suggestions/comments

If a hoist is unacceptable and a rotunda is impractical because the client does not have the necessary arm strength, a lower risk method of transfer onto the turntable is for two care workers to sit on either side on the bed and to use a padded, non-slip handling belt with handles and assist the client up to the standing position.

In some instances a 'Jackson commode' or a similar bed-fitting commode, may be more suitable, especially if the client is able to use upper limb strength to slide themself onto the commode. This piece of equipment is especially useful too when considering clients at risk of falling, when taking themselves to the toilet at night.

Helping a client onto the toilet

Task

Mrs B lived with her husband but had communication problems following a stroke, affecting the right side of her body. She used a wheelchair and needed assistance with all transfers, including getting on and off the toilet. The bathroom had been adapted so that there was enough space on both sides of the toilet for Mrs B to always transfer through her unaffected side. Her husband helped her to transfer by standing in front of her and providing minimal assistance.

Manual handling problem

Mrs B started to visit a day care centre. Unfortunately, the toilets at the centre were all positioned next to a wall and Mrs B was not able to transfer between her wheelchair and the toilet using her unaffected side. The day care centre staff were unable to manually assist Mrs B with this task and suggested using a hoist. However, Mrs B was making good progress with rehabilitation and both she and her husband did not want this progress to be lost. They were, therefore, reluctant to accept the use of the hoist. The care manager was alerted and an occupational therapist was called in to assess the situation.

Control measures

The occupational therapist found a large bathroom which had a handrail against a free wall. There was enough space in the bathroom to allow Mrs B to transfer from her wheelchair onto a mobile commode (with the bowl removed) which could then be wheeled over the toilet. When Mrs B needed to go to the toilet, two care workers would wheel her into the bathroom, position her in front of the handrail and then stand either side of her to give her confidence and provide any assistance necessary. Mrs B would then hold the rail with her unaffected hand and pull herself to a standing position. Initially, the care workers were issued with a handling belt to offer Mrs B assistance in rising but, as she grew more confident, Mrs B was able to get up unaided. Once Mrs B was standing, the care worker on her unaffected side would move the wheelchair from behind her and replace it with the mobile commode. The other care worker, on Mrs B's affected side, stood ready to help and give Mrs B a feeling of security. Once the mobile commode was in place, the care workers adjusted Mrs B's clothing. Mrs B then lowered herself onto the commode. The care workers then wheeled the commode over the toilet.

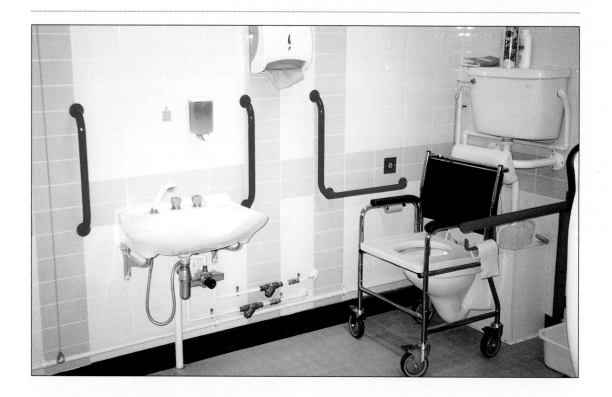

Cost

There were no costs incurred as the day centre already had an existing mobile commode which Mrs B could use.

Benefits

The manual handling risk to the care workers from the transfer to the commode/toilet was minimised and the care workers had sufficient space to assist Mrs B safely.

Mrs B was happy with the arrangement. She was able to continue attending the day care centre and using the handrail meant she could stand and maintain the progress she had made during her rehabilitation sessions.

In addition, the solution enabled Mrs B to maintain her dignity. She did not need to be hoisted over the toilet and the large bathroom allowed her clothing to be adjusted in privacy.

Using a toileting shell

Task

Mr E had cerebral palsy. He was unable to communicate verbally, although understood other people's speech. He lived in a nursing home and had his own room, but was totally dependent on care workers for his personal care. Care workers were available to assist him at all hours. In his own home, Mr E had used a moulded plastic shell with an aperture for toileting which he used with a hoist. He brought this with him to the nursing home.

Manual handling problem

When Mr E wanted to go to the toilet, two care workers leant over the bed in a stooped posture and assisted him into the toileting shell. They attached the shell to the mobile hoist and pushed him the short distance to the en suite bathroom. The care workers then positioned

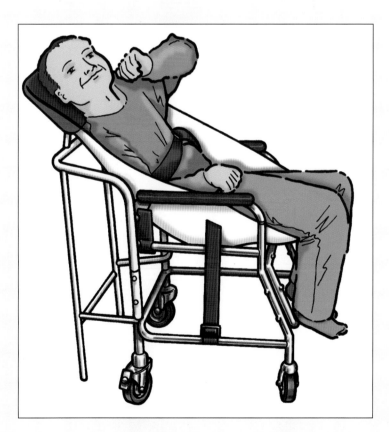

the shell over the toilet and lowered Mr E onto the toilet. The care workers found the task difficult and discussed their concerns with Mr E's social worker. She contacted the occupational therapist who visited the home to review the risk assessment.

Control measures

The occupational therapist identified the manual handling risk to the care workers from the stooping, reaching over the bed and assisting Mr E into the shell. There was also a further risk of injury from moving the mobile hoist in a confined area. Mr E was also at risk from the awkward postures needed to get him into the shell and from swinging in the hoist. In addition, Mr E was prone to extensor spasms and there was a risk that he could fall out of the shell.

As a result of the risk assessment review, the method of transfer was changed. An updated shell was bought. With this, Mr E could transfer to the shell by being rolled onto a sling and hoisted rather than lifted. In addition, the shell was fitted onto a mobile base and angled to minimise the risk of him falling out if he had a extensor spasm. The mobile base was easy to move and fitted over the toilet without difficulty.

Cost

The cost of the new shell was about £700.

Benefits

The manual handling risk to the care workers from stooping, stretching and lifting Mr E into the shell was removed. The risk of injury to Mr E from the awkward postures needed to get him into the old shell were reduced and he was no longer in danger of falling out of the shell.

The mobile base was smaller and easier to manoeuvre in the confined space. This helped to reduce the manual handling risk to the care workers from moving the hoist and the risk of injury to Mr E from swinging in the hoist.

Additional suggestions/comments

While waiting for delivery of the new shell, the risk of injury to the care workers and to Mr E could be reduced by fitting the existing shell over the toilet and using a sling that allowed Mr E to remain in a sitting position. This would have allowed Mr E to be hoisted onto the shell without the need for stooping, reaching and lifting and minimised the risk of extensor spasms.

Adaptations to the toilet

Task

Mr M had muscular dystrophy. He weighed about 16 stone/100 kg. His house had been adapted for him and two care workers attended daily to assist with toileting.

Manual handling problem

Mr M was transferred from his bed to the toilet using a ceiling track hoist. The ceiling track was installed at 90° to the bed and toilet. As a result Mr M had to be positioned high up the bed in order to be hoisted comfortably. The care workers had to pull him up the bed into this position before attaching the sling straps to the hoist. Once in the sling Mr M controlled the movement of the hoist from the bed to the bathroom and was assisted in lining up the sling over the toilet seat below him. Mr M's head was

supported manually by the care workers to avoid collision with the door frame between bedroom and bathroom. Once on the toilet seat, one care worker supported his body while the other moved a wheelchair next to him to provide additional support. The sling straps were then disconnected. The care workers were unhappy with pulling Mr M up the bed before hoisting and reported this to their manual handling advisor. The manual handling advisor reviewed the risk assessment and identified a number of problems:

- Risks of injury to the care workers and Mr M from pulling up the bed; risk of injury to the care worker while supporting Mr M on the toilet; and risk of injury to Mr M from using the wheelchair for support;
- Issues of client dignity.

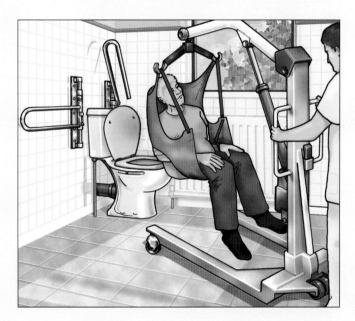

Control measures

The manual handling advisor recommended that slide sheets be provided to move Mr M up the bed into a suitable position for hoisting. Once Mr M was lying on the sheets the care workers stood either side of the bed with one knee at his shoulder level and their other foot on the floor in front of them. The care workers could then simultaneously pull gently on the handles of the sheet to slide Mr M up the bed. As Mr M had little head control and his upper body was weak a sling with a head support was provided. This was a standard sling with an additional piece of material at the top with 'bones' in the back to support his head in an upright position. To provide support two adjustable support rails were installed on either side of the toilet. These were lowered by the care workers once Mr M was seated on the toilet and fitted securely under his arms. The rails supported his upper body while seated and ensured he was secure and stable. He could then be left alone to use the toilet.

Cost

The cost of the support rails was about £120 and the sling with head support cost £170.

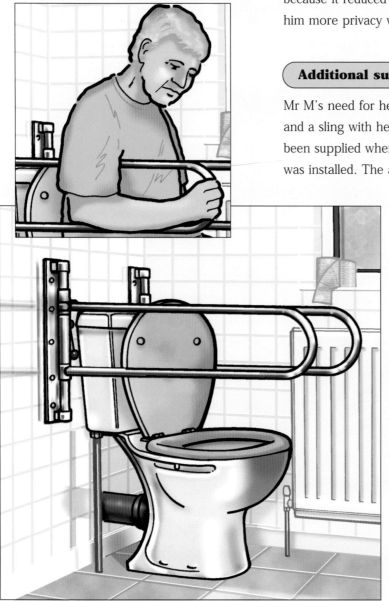

Benefits

By reducing the effort needed to reposition Mr M in bed, the slide sheets reduced the manual handling risk to the care workers and Mr M; the support rails eliminated the need for the care workers to support Mr M on the toilet; and the sling with head support helped prevent Mr M injuring himself on the door frame when moving between bedroom and bathroom.

Mr M was happy with the solution because it reduced his risk of injury and gave him more privacy while toileting.

Additional suggestions/comments

Mr M's need for head support was obvious and a sling with head support should have been supplied when the ceiling track hoist was installed. The appropriateness of the original risk assessment, therefore, must be questioned.

As a short-term measure, while waiting for the rails to be fitted in the bathroom, an appropriately sized mobile commode with side arms could have been used in the bedroom.

Washing and toileting a client

Task

Mrs D was very frail and weighed about 7 stone/45 kg. She had paper-thin skin which bled and bruised easily. An electric hoist with overhead tracking was used for all transfers. Mrs D needed to shower at least twice weekly and, for religious reasons, had to be washed in running water after toileting. Two care workers visited Mrs D twice a day to assist with these tasks.

Manual handling problem

The shower/toilet chair used was made of hard plastic, with a gap in the front centre. Mrs D's deteriorating condition meant that the chair was no longer suitable. She would regularly slip forward on the chair, especially when showering, and fall to one side, trapping her leg in the gap of the chair. She was at risk from bruising/tearing of the skin when she got her leg caught in the gap and the care workers were at high risk of injury from the constant need to lift her back onto the chair several times during showering. The care workers alerted their home care organiser to the problem.

Control measures

The home care organiser visited Mrs D's home to update the manual handling risk assessment. A high risk to the care workers was identified and the showering was stopped until a more suitable shower/toilet chair could be provided. The new shower/toilet chair was padded with no gap in the middle and this allowed Mrs D to sit in a better posture. Meantime, Mrs D was washed in bed but this short-term solution caused further problems. The bed was too low and care workers had to stoop to wash her. To overcome this problem, a hospital bed was provided which could be raised when Mrs D was bed washed.

Benefits

The new shower/toilet chair prevented Mrs D from trapping her leg and also reduced the risk of her slipping off the chair and removed the risk to the care workers from handling/assisting her. The new chair also reduced the risk of injury to Mrs D.

Raising the bed reduced the manual handling risk to care workers as they were no longer required to work in a stooped posture.

The time required for showering/toileting was reduced because the care workers no longer had to spend time assisting Mrs D back into the seat.

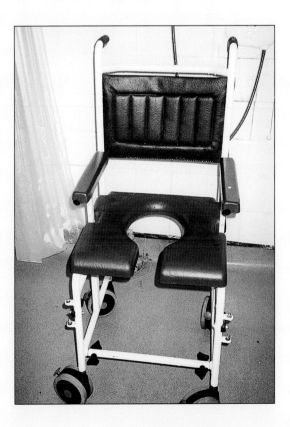

Additional suggestions/comments

This case shows up a number of deficiencies:

- the review of the risk assessment should have identified the need for bed raisers as part of its recommendation for bed baths;

- a basic £750 rise and fall bed might have been considered rather than the more costly hospital bed, which costs around £2000; and

- high dependency cases, such as Mrs D's, should be discussed with the care workers regularly and the risk assessment reviewed as often as once a month, if necessary, to make sure that arrangements are still appropriate. In this case, such a review would have highlighted the problems with the shower/toilet chair much earlier.

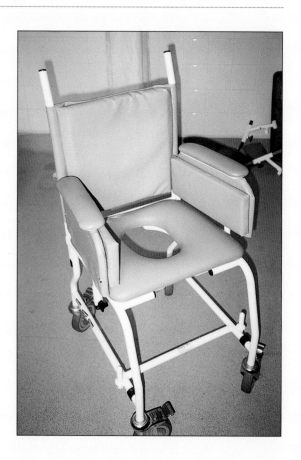

Reducing risks in a bathroom

Task

Mrs S had experienced a stroke and needed help to stand and move about the house. When she came home after six weeks in hospital, she was given a wheelchair to help with mobility and, because of the distance between the bed and the toilet, a care worker visited twice a day to assist with toileting.

Manual handling problem

During a routine visit to assess the care plan package, the care manager was concerned about several aspects of the toileting task. To get Mrs S to the bathroom, the care worker had to push the wheelchair along a carpeted hall. The bathroom door opened inwards and there was a large wash basin and wall cabinet. This made it difficult for the care worker to get in to help Mrs S onto the toilet. To move from the wheelchair to the toilet, Mrs S pulled herself up with the help of the care worker who then twisted her round onto the toilet. Once finished on the toilet, Mrs S had to stand so that the care worker could clean her and replace her clothing. The toilet roll and cleaning cloths were often placed at a distance from the toilet and the carer had to twist and bend to reach it, while supporting Mrs S. In addition, the toilet was at a low level and, to stand up, Mrs S had to pull on the care worker.

A formal assessment by the manual handling advisor identified a number of risk elements in the task:

- pushing the wheelchair over thick carpet;
- twisting, pulling and stretching in the confined space in the bathroom;

- supporting Mrs S to stand and twisting her round onto the toilet;
- twisting, bending and supporting Mrs S to move off the toilet and into the wheelchair.

Control measures

To reduce the risks the following changes were made:

- the thick pile carpet in the hall was replaced with linoleum. The smooth surface helped reduce the effort needed to push the wheelchair to the bathroom;
- the space in the bathroom was increased by replacing the swing door with a sliding door, exchanging the wash basin for a smaller unit and moving the wall cabinet to another room;
- appropriately positioned handrails and grips were provided to enable Mrs S to pull herself up from the wheelchair/toilet and to help her support herself during cleaning;
- the toilet roll and cleaning cloths were moved onto the cistern before toileting so that it was easier for the care worker to reach them when needed;
- a raised toilet seat was provided so that Mrs S could stand up more easily and the side of the wheelchair was removed to make transfer easier. A turntable was provided to turn Mrs S when getting onto the toilet and to transfer her to the wheelchair after toileting;
- the care worker was given appropriate training in good handling techniques and in how to recognise and deal with handling risks;

- in addition, the care worker was encouraged to dress appropriately for easy movement, including wearing non-slip and sensible footwear, and encouraged to report any musculoskeletal disorders, no matter how they were caused.

Cost

Modifications to the bathroom cost approximately £350 and the manual handling training for the care workers, including annual renewal training, cost around £88 per year.

Benefits

The manual handling risk to the care worker was reduced because Mrs S was able to raise and lower herself onto the toilet with little or no assistance.

The extra space in the bathroom and taking care that the cleaning materials were easy to get at made the toileting task faster and easier.

Mrs S was happy because the changes made her feel more independent.

Additional suggestions/comments

When Mrs S was discharged from hospital following her stroke, the care plan should have identified the risks with delivering the toileting and bathing services safely. Though linoleum was used in this case, there are other alternatives to carpeting to help reduce pushing and pulling wheelchairs, hoists etc.

Transfer to the toilet

Task

Mrs G was confused and her behaviour was occasionally unpredictable. She was not very mobile and needed assistance with getting out of bed, with personal care and with dressing. She weighed about 8 stone/50 kg. She was cared for by a relative and a care worker.

Manual handling problem

To transfer Mrs G from her bed involved moving her from a low, soft divan to a higher armchair, positioned near the bed. This task involved stooping to raise Mrs G from the edge of the bed to a standing position. The care worker and carer needed to support Mrs G as she shuffled to the chair and both the care worker and carer twisted to support Mrs G as she lowered herself into the chair. Sometimes Mrs G would move suddenly and it would be difficult for the care worker and carer to maintain their hold on her. Once she was seated in the armchair, the care worker or carer pushed the chair to the bathroom and then transferred Mrs G to the toilet. The care worker reported shoulder and neck problems after attending to Mrs G. A manual handling advisor was called in to review the risk assessment.

Control measures

The risk assessment identified the risk of injury to the care worker, the carer and Mrs G from the hazardous lifting and supporting and recommended raising the bed using blocks and inserting a board underneath the mattress. This provided a firm base from which to transfer Mrs G as well as a more suitable height in relation to the chair. With Mrs G's agreement, a mobile hoist, such as that illustrated in Case Study 6, was installed for transfer from the bed to the chair. This eliminated the need to raise and support Mrs G manually. A wheelchair was also supplied to move Mrs G more safely and easily around the house. A mobile commode (glide-about) was also provided (see Case Study 15 for a photograph of a mobile commode), so that Mrs G could sit on the commode and be pushed to the bathroom into position over the toilet.

Cost

The costs involved were around £400 for the hoist and £100 for the mobile commode.

Benefits

The manual handling risks to both the care worker and the carer were reduced. Raising the height of the bed removed the need for the care worker and carer to adopt awkward

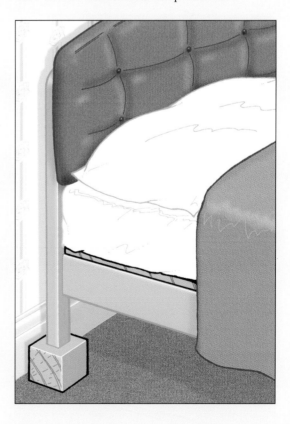

postures when assisting Mrs G in bed; the hoist and wheelchair removed the need to assist and support Mrs G during transfers; and the mobile commode, which could be positioned over the toilet, eliminated the manual handling involved in transferring Mrs G onto the toilet.

Additional suggestions/comments

Carpeting can make it difficult to manoeuvre hoists and wheelchairs. If this were a problem in Mrs G's home, the carpeting could be replaced with linoleum or some other suitable floor covering to provide the smooth floor surface that makes it easier to move the hoist when it is not in use, and reduces the effort needed to push the wheelchair.

A competent risk assessment at the time the care plan was drawn up would have identified all these problems before the care worker was sent in. All equipment should have been in place when the care plan was put in place.

Moving around the house

Handling task

Helping a client to get round their home.

Hazards

Hazards can arise from the carpets, narrow doorways, high door sills; confined space; unpredictable client behaviour; clients with limited ability to support their own weight; care workers carrying out uncoordinated transfers. A significant hazard also arises from the condition and maintenance of equipment used.

Risks

The risk will be to both the care worker and the client:

- The care worker is at risk of back and neck injury from the need to adopt awkward postures (stooping, bending, and twisting) and pulling the client up into the standing or lowering to the sitting position during transfers; from pushing wheelchairs, mobile commodes, hoists over thick pile carpeting; manoeuvring mobile hoists through narrow spaces; from trying to take sudden remedial action when a client is unable to support their own weight and starts to fall.

- The client is at risk of shoulder injury from pulling up into the standing position or lowering to the sitting position; of bruising or worse from falling, or from collisions with furniture and fittings.

Control measures

The risks can be avoided or minimised in a number of ways, eg a more appropriate flooring (linoleum/parquet instead of carpeting); handling aids; repositioning of furniture etc, depending on the particular circumstances. Regular maintenance of mobility equipment must be undertaken to ensure its continued effectiveness. Case studies 18-23 demonstrate how others have tackled these challenges.

Transfers between rooms

Task

Mrs F had experienced a severe stroke which affected her right side. She had made a good recovery and was mobile over short distances, but tired easily. Her husband was her main carer and a care worker visited once a day to assist.

Manual handling problem

To get around the house, Mr F would walk beside his wife to give her confidence but, as she got weaker, she would increasingly use Mr F as a support. She weighed around 10 stone/65 kg and Mr F found it difficult to support her. Mrs F also sometimes needed assistance to get up from her chair and on and off the toilet. To do this, the care worker and Mr F would pull on her arms to help her into a standing position, which is a very unsafe and inappropriate technique. There was a high risk of damage to Mrs F's arm/shoulder during this manoeuvre and also a risk to Mr F and the care worker from supporting Mrs F's weight. Mr F raised these problems with the district nurse and she called in an occupational therapist to review the risk assessment.

Control measures

A mobile commode or 'glide-about' with a seat added on top was provided to help Mrs F to move between rooms without support. It also allowed Mrs F to use it as a dining chair when necessary. With the seat removed, the commode could be pushed over the toilet for toileting. A handling belt was also provided to support Mrs F when she got on and off the seat/commode. With the belt on, Mrs F used both arms to push herself up and Mr F and the care worker gripped the belt to assist her if required.

Cost

The cost of the mobile commode was approximately £150 and the handling belt £30.

Benefits

The risk of back injury to Mr F and the care worker was reduced and the transfers were faster and safer for Mrs F. In particular, her arms were no longer being pulled to help her stand up and the risk of falling while walking from room to room was eliminated.

Additional suggestions/comments

It is surprising that the original manual handling risk assessment did not identify the benefits to everyone of using the handling belt and commode. Handling belts are usually readily available and there is not normally a long wait for a commode.

Physiotherapy may be a solution to maintain her mobility. She could be taught to walk with a quadrapod or might be able to manoeuvre a self-propelled wheelchair in the house with her unaffected arm and steer with her unaffected leg. This may help to maintain her independence and might be more comfortable and pleasant to sit on than a mobile commode chair. Grab rails in different rooms could be positioned to allow her to pull herself up into standing and transfer from wheelchair to armchair.

Using a stand-aid to help standing and transfers

Task

Mrs E had experienced a stroke which left her with a weakness on one side. She was recently discharged from hospital and needed help with transfers, particularly to stand. Two care workers visited her twice a day.

Manual handling problem

To help Mrs E transfer from, eg her chair to the wheelchair/commode/bed, the care workers used a turntable. Mrs E would hold on to the care worker's arms to help pull herself up from the chair and stand on the turntable. They would then support her and turn her so that she was positioned over the wheelchair/commode/bed ready for lowering. Often the care workers would need to bend over Mrs E to help pull her to a standing position and as the turntable had no brakes Mrs E would begin to turn as she stood up. This caused the care workers to twist, increasing the risk of injury. Sometimes Mrs E would hurt the care workers as she held very tightly onto their arms to pull herself off the chair. The care workers realised that there was a problem with the care plan and asked the occupational therapist to visit the home. The occupational therapist reviewed the risk assessment and identified a high manual handling risk to the care workers from pulling Mrs E to standing and supporting her weight as she turned on the turntable.

Control measures

A hoist could have helped Mrs E with transfer tasks but neither Mrs E or her husband wanted this for fear that it would hinder Mrs E's rehabilitation and reduce her standing

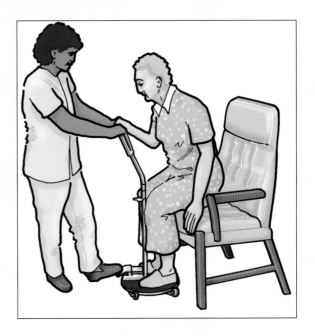

tolerance. An alternative solution was to introduce a stand-aid (turntable with a handle) to reduce the manual handling effort required to raise Mrs E. With the stand-aid, Mrs E was able to put her feet on the turntable while she sat in the chair, hold onto the handle and pull herself into a standing position using her strong arm. The stand-aid had a brake on the turntable, so it would not move while Mrs E pulled herself up. The care worker then released the brake on the turntable and used the handle to turn her gently. Mrs E supported herself on the handle as she was being turned.

Cost

The cost of the stand-aid was approximately £200.

Benefits

The stand-aid reduced the manual handling risk of injury to the care workers. It also removed the need for some of the handling tasks so that only one care worker was needed to assist Mrs E.

Both Mr and Mrs E were happy because Mrs E was using her muscles to stand and did not lose her standing tolerance. In addition, Mr E was able to use the stand-aid to toilet his wife at night, so that she did not need a catheter.

Additional suggestions/comments

If the chair is low, it may be difficult for a person to pull themselves up to a standing position. It might be helpful, therefore, to raise the height of a chair using blocks beneath the chair legs or extension legs which fit around the chair legs. It is vital, however, to make sure that the blocks or extensions do not make the chair unstable. Alternatively, providing the client with a cushion to raise the height or firmness of the chair is also useful.

The stand-aid would need to be used in conjunction with the right height of chair, otherwise care workers will be involved in helping her to stand.

The care workers' problem with the turntable shows poor manual handling training. Care workers who are expected to use turntables should be taught to use the equipment properly.

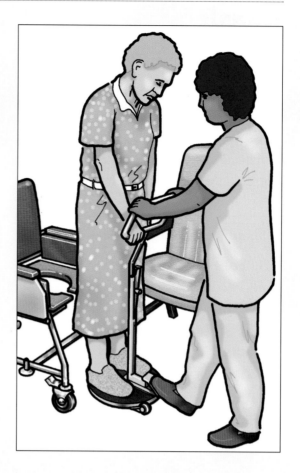

Assisting a child after a fall

Task

Miss C, aged 9, suffered from a genetic hormonal disorder which caused excessive weight gain, learning difficulties and recurring epileptic seizures. She lived at home with her mother who was the primary carer.

Manual handling problem

Following an epileptic seizure, Miss C needed to be helped up from the floor, but this was a difficult task. Mrs C would lift her daughter off the floor unaided but found this difficult because Miss C weighed over 10 stone/65 kg and, though co-operative, was generally unable to give help. The task involved considerable effort and aggravated Mrs C's long-term back injury. An occupational therapist recognised the risks to the carer and referred the case to a back care advisor to review the risk assessment.

Control measures

The back care advisor recommended the use of an emergency lifting cushion and the family bought a powered lifting cushion. When transferring Miss C from the floor, Mrs C rolled her daughter onto the cushion and air was pumped into it from a portable battery powered compressor. As the cushion inflated, Miss C was raised into the sitting position. To maintain stability, Mrs C stood behind her daughter and supported her as she was rising. Once the cushion had inflated, Mrs C held her daughter's hands and she was able to stand with minimal assistance.

Cost

The cost of the cushion was around £815. It is important, however, to take expert advice on relevance and suitability when buying equipment independently.

Benefits

The powered lifting cushion eliminated a manual handling task and reduced the risk of further damage to Mrs C's back.

Additional suggestions/comments

Though this solution was adequate, an alternative option might have been a cushion with a back rest. This would have provided greater support as the cushion inflated.

Mrs C's back condition should have been acknowledged in the development of the care plan and a competent risk assessment done to minimise risk.

Where extreme difficulty is encountered with moving a person who is in spasm, it would be advisable to seek an assessment from a physiotherapist.

Reducing risks by modifying living arrangements

Task

Miss N, an 18-year old with spina bifida, lived at home and was cared for by her parents. The family lived in a two-storey house and the parents insisted that their daughter slept upstairs. They carried their daughter up and down stairs twice daily. As Miss N grew older and heavier the risk assessment was reviewed and a hoist or stair lift was recommended to reduce the risk of injury. The parents, however, refused the offer and continued to use manual transfer techniques until Miss N's mother suffered a back injury. Two care workers then visited to assist with the transfers.

Manual handling problem

The care package was reassessed and a problem of helping Miss N transfer safely between bed and chair and up and down stairs was identified. Account was also taken of the short-term needs of the care workers as well as the longer term implications of Miss N's parents continuing care for their daughter at home.

Solution

The short-term solution was to move Miss N's bed down to the ground floor and eliminate the need to carry her up and down the stairs. With Miss N and her parent's consent, a mobile hoist was provided to help transfer Miss N between her bed and a wheelchair. The long-term solution was to establish a purpose-built extension to the house for Miss N. The additional accommodation comprised a bedroom with adjoining shower and toilet. Overhead tracking for ceiling hoists was installed through both areas to eliminate the need to transfer Miss N manually between rooms.

Cost

The cost of the shorter term solution included £3500 for the ceiling track hoist and £200 per week for two care workers. It is appreciated that the long-term solution in this case would not be practical in most situations and has, therefore, not been costed.

Benefits

The short-term solution reduced the risk of injury to the care workers and the carers. It also avoided the need for respite care in hospital and allowed Miss N to stay at home while her mother's injured back healed.

The long-term solution eliminated most of the manual handling risk to her parents and ensured that there was a suitable environment for Miss N's future needs.

Additional suggestions/comments

To ensure maximum benefit from the shorter term solution, arrangements would need to be made to ensure that the bed was moved downstairs on the same day that the hoist was installed.

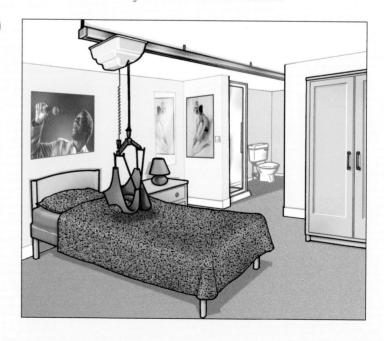

Adapting a sling for use by a heavy client

Task

Miss O had spina bifida and lived alone in her own bungalow. She was a wheelchair user and her condition was deteriorating. She was totally dependent on a complex care package involving a district nurse, two care workers (twice a day) and a bath service. Miss O weighed over 19 stone/126 kg. She needed to be in a semi-reclined position because she was unable to bend from the waist. She had a problem with fluid retention around her legs and ankles. When touching her skin she was prone to pressure sores and skin tearing.

Manual handling problem

There was a gantry hoist in the bedroom, but there were increasing problems putting the standard sling on because of her size. In addition, the sling was causing Miss O discomfort when she was being moved. One of the main challenges was that, due to her weight, the care workers could not safely roll Miss O onto the sling. Instead, they had to pull on Miss O's arm and shoulders, to bring her forward so that they could put the sling behind her. This manoeuvre posed a threat to Miss O's skin condition and a manual handling risk to the care workers.

Control measures

An occupational therapist reviewed the situation and recommended a special sling, similar to a toileting sling, of appropriate size and material. The hole in the back of the sling helped prevent pressure on Miss O's spine. The sheepskin lining on the legs reduced the discomfort Miss O felt during lifting. The sling was easier to use because the care workers were able to push Miss O's shoulders from behind to tuck the sling behind her. The sling

was usually left on to reduce the handling problems associated with putting the sling on. This was Miss O's preference to avoid the need for repeated handling. When she was not being hoisted, Miss O would undo the straps that went around her chest and tuck the free material of the sling over her wheelchair or chair.

To make it easier to dress Miss O with the sling on, her clothing was adapted, so it opened at the back and could therefore be easily put on from the front. The clothes were held together at the back with Velcro which was accessible through the gap in the back of the sling.

Cost

The cost of the adapted sling was about £200.

Benefits

After some initial misgivings about the use of the new sling, Miss O agreed to the changes because it reduced the manual handling risk to the care workers.

In use, however, Miss O found that the new sling made hoisting more comfortable. She also found that by keeping the sling on all day, she did not have to be handled as much which was safer for her skin.

Additional suggestions/comments

Taking into account Miss O's size and medical condition, a rise and fall bed with an elevator may have been considered to help Miss O sit up. This would reduce the risk associated with fitting a sling.

It is not clear why the risk assessment when the gantry hoist was being introduced did not identify the need for an appropriate and properly fitting sling.

Moving a wheelchair into the garden

Task

Mrs C had severe multiple sclerosis and lived at home with her 90-year old mother. She spent most of her time in a wheelchair. An occupational therapist visited regularly and care workers visited three times a day to help with personal care and to assist Mrs C in and out of bed. During the day, Mrs C's mother helped her move from room to room in the wheelchair. Mrs C weighed approximately 8 stone/50 kg.

Manual handling problem

Though Mrs C's mother could manage the move from room to room, she had difficulty moving her daughter into the garden because the patio door had a large sill and she could not push the wheelchair through the doorway.

Control measures

Mrs C discussed the problem of access to the garden with the occupational therapist and arrangements were made with the social works department to install a fibreglass mini-ramp over the frame sill.

Cost

The ramp cost approximately £70.

Benefits

The ramp reduced Mrs C's mother's risk of injury from the strenuous pushing and pulling to move the wheelchair into the garden. It also enabled the smooth travel of the wheelchair into the garden.

The ramp was very light and easy to put in place and could be removed when not needed.

Additional suggestions/comments

The assessment of Mrs C's needs were not looked at comprehensively when the wheelchair was first recommended. Had this been done, the manual handling problems of access to the garden would have been identified.

Also, an indoor/outdoor electric chair might have helped here too.

Managing the stairs

Handling task

Helping a client to go up and down stairs.

Hazards

Hazards can arise from the confined space at the top and bottom of the staircase; unpredictable client behaviour; clients with limited ability to support their own weight and uncoordinated lifting assistance for care workers.

Risks

The risk will be to both the care worker and the client:

- The care worker is at risk of back and neck injury from the need to adopt awkward postures (stooping, bending, and twisting) and assisting the client up into the standing or lowering to the sitting position; from trying to take sudden remedial action when a client is unable to support their own weight and starts to fall.
- The client is at risk of shoulder injury from assisting up into the standing position or lowering to the sitting position; of bruising or worse from falling.

Control measures

The risks can be avoided or minimised in a number of ways, eg an appropriately designed stair lift; handling aids etc, depending on the particular circumstances. Case study 24 demonstrates how others have tackled these challenges.

Transferring a child onto a stair lift in a confined space

Task

Miss M, a teenager, had severe learning difficulties and was unable to speak. She spent a lot of her time in a wheelchair and was dependent on carers for most of her needs. She lived at home with her mother, who was her main carer, and went to school while her mother was out at work. Miss M weighed about 8 stone/50 kg and was larger than her mother.

Manual handling problem

Miss M needed assistance to get from the ground floor of the house to the kitchen in the basement. A stair lift was installed to transport her down the stairs. To do this, the wheelchair was manoeuvred to the top of the stairs and Mrs M then lifted her daughter into the stair lift. The area at the top of the stairs, however, was very constricted and there was little space to turn the wheelchair. The need for manual lifting in a restricted space presented a risk of injury to the carer and there was also a risk of the carer falling down the stairs while transferring her daughter.

Control measures

During a routine visit, the occupational therapist noticed the problem and reviewed the risk assessment. The use of a mobile hoist was considered, but the space at the top of the stairs was too confined for this. Instead, an electrically operated ceiling (overhead tracking) hoist was installed to help transfer Miss M from the wheelchair into the stair lift at the top of the stairs. The wheelchair was placed under the hoist in an area where it was safe for the carer to fit the sling. The carer could then secure Miss M in the stair lift without the space constraints at the top of the stairs.

Cost

The cost of the ceiling track hoist was £495.

Benefits

The manual handling risk to the carer was reduced and the danger of the carer falling down the stairs was removed. Miss M enjoyed being hoisted and travelling on the stair lift.

Additional suggestions/comments

Stair lifts are the normal solution, if it is not feasible for the client to be cared for on the same level. However, they are not always appropriate, particularly if the stairway is narrow. In such cases, a 'thro floor' lift could be considered.

It is difficult to understand why the ceiling track was not installed at the same time as the stair lift. The appropriateness of the manual handling risk assessment at the time of fitting the stair lift must be questioned.

Assisting into and out of the car

Handling task

Helping a client to get into and out of the car.

Hazards

Hazards can arise from the restricted access to the standard car; unpredictable client behaviour; clients with limited ability to support their own weight; uncoordinated lifting assistance for care workers, and the low height of car seats.

Risks

Both the care worker and the client are at risk:

- The care worker is at risk of back and neck injury from the need to adopt awkward postures (stooping, bending, and twisting) and assisting the client up into the standing or lowering to the sitting position; stooping to lift the client's legs into or out of the car; and from trying to take sudden remedial action when a client is unable to support their own weight and starts to fall.

- The client is at risk of shoulder injury from assisting up into the standing position or lowering to the sitting position; of bruising or worse from falling.

Control measures

The risks can be avoided or minimised in a number of ways, eg a specialised car; using appropriate handling aids etc, depending on the particular circumstances. Case studies 25–27 demonstrate how others have tackled these challenges.

Using a thigh lifter and turntable to help a client into a car

Task

Mr H had severe rheumatoid arthritis and was cared for by his wife. He was able to walk short distances with assistance and his wife pushed him in a wheelchair when they went out. Mrs H, however, was elderly, suffered from poor eyesight and was unable to drive. Mr H held a current driving licence but had difficulty getting into and out of the car. Maintaining the ability to drive was important to the couple, because it meant that they could continue to go shopping together and visit friends and relatives.

A care worker came on a weekly basis to assist normally with bathing and household duties, but this involved minimal manual handling. To maintain independance it was important for the couple that Mr H maintained the ability to drive, but he had difficulty in getting in and out of the car due to reduced strength and joint mobility in his legs and spine.

Manual handling problem

To get into the car, Mrs H supported her husband while he lowered himself in. There had been a minor accident, however, when she had not been able to hold him and he had hit his head on the doorway of the car. Since then, Mrs H was reluctant to help her husband into the car and they asked the care worker to help. The care worker was concerned with the risk of injury to herself and Mr H while supporting his weight in a stooped position.

Control measures

The care and risk assessment at the local mobility centre evaluated both Mr H's driving and his transfer requirements. To solve the transfer problem, a thigh lifter was fitted to the driver's seat which mechanically lifted and lowered Mr H. In addition, a turntable was

placed on the seat to allow Mr H to turn into and out of the car independently. For safety reasons, this had to be removed after the transfer into the car. Mrs H was able to help with this and to replace it when Mr H wanted to get out of the car.

Cost

The thigh lifter cost £900 and the turntable £40.

Benefits

The new equipment helped to reduce the manual handling risk, by minimising the effort involved in getting Mr H in and out of the driver's seat.

In addition, the couple were able to continue to use the car independently in safety. The level of care required by Mr H was kept to a minimum and thus costs reduced.

Additional suggestions/comments

The care worker was right to carry out duties that Mr and Mrs H would normally have carried out with the use of a car until the equipment was in place. But, the problem with access to the car should have been picked up much earlier by the risk assessment.

Using a swivel person hoist to help a client into a car

Task

Mrs Y had bilateral below knee amputations and was cared for by her husband and the district nursing service. The couple tried to be as independent as possible and Mrs Y required nursing care only for dressing of pressure sores. The local back care advisor had assessed the manual handling requirements of the couple and a mobile hoist was used to assist with transfers in the home.

Manual handling problem

Mrs Y's husband helped her with transfers from the wheelchair to the car, using a transfer board and transfer belt. The district nurse, however, became increasingly concerned about the manual handling risk to Mr Y as Mrs Y became less able to assist with the manoeuvre. She was concerned, too, that the practice of putting the board in place and sliding along it was a skin care risk to Mrs Y and could result in the development of further areas of broken skin.

Control measures

The reassessment at the local mobility centre, to evaluate the driving and Mrs Y's transfer requirements, recommended the installation of an electric swivel person hoist into the passenger side of the car. This equipment is designed to lift the person from a wheelchair into a car seat.

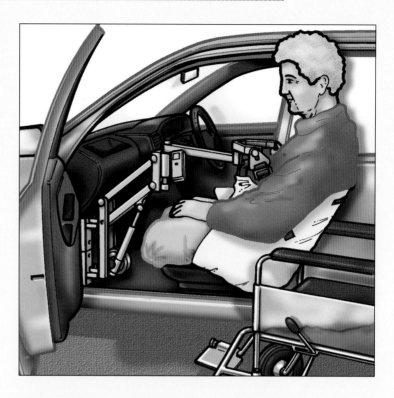

Cost

The electric swivel person hoist cost £1800.

Benefits

The hoist eliminated the manual handling risk to Mr Y when transferring his wife from her wheelchair to the car.

Mrs Y was happy because it allowed her to continue to go out in the car with minimal risks to her husband and to her own skin. This minimised the level of care required and maximised their independence.

Additional suggestions/comments

Until the electric swivel person hoist is fitted, Mr Y should be advised not to take his wife out in the car.

Transporting a child in a car

Task

Miss H was 14. She weighed over 4 stone/25 kg and was 1.6 m tall. She had cerebral palsy and was cared for at home by her mother and father, who were her primary carers. Care workers visited the home three times a day to assist with personal care. Miss H was unable to assist with moving and needed help with all transfers. The family had a standard car which Mr H used to take his daughter to the Day Care Centre and respite care.

Manual handling problem

Miss H's parents were reluctant to use manual handling equipment and the home care manager was unable to provide help with lifting because of the risk to the care workers. Mr and Mrs H, therefore, lifted their daughter during all transfers from bed to wheelchair, wheelchair to bath, wheelchair to car, etc. To get her into the car, her parents would lift Miss H from her wheelchair and, while supporting her, bend and place her in the car. They would then lift the wheelchair into the boot. Mrs H injured her back while lifting her daughter.

Control measures

The social worker spoke again about the possibility of using a hoist to transfer Miss H. During a visit to the Children's Centre Mr and Mrs H saw how easy a hoist made lifting and decided to try one out. Miss H went to hospital for major surgery to her spine. As a temporary solution, a hoist was loaned from the Children's Centre for use when she returned home until more permanent arrangements could be made. A mesh sling was also purchased to be used when bathing Miss H. The couple kept the sling on Miss H during the day to minimise the need for handling.

Following the operation Miss H needed
to maintain a 90° angle when sitting. Her
parents found it difficult to arrange this in their
car and an adapted vehicle with adequate
space for a wheelchair was purchased. Miss
H's parents were then able to open the back
of the vehicle, lift down the ramp and wheel
Miss H in. During the six months it took for
the new car to be delivered, a special Children's
Centre bus picked up Miss H from her home
and took her to the Centre.

Cost

The hoist cost around £2000 and the mesh
sling £90.

Benefits

The hoist reduced the risk of injury to Miss
H's parents and she liked using it because she
was no longer being manhandled and when
she was being hoisted she felt it was like being
on a swing. In addition, the burden of care
was reduced because the care workers were
now able to help with transfers.

Mr and Mrs H were happy with the
adapted vehicle because Miss H could stay
seated in her wheelchair and maintain the
necessary 90° angle. There was now much
less physical effort needed to transport Miss H
and this allowed her parents to take her to a
lot more activity groups.

The legal framework

1 Community Care legislation requires the development of care plans to cover the needs of clients and how that care should be delivered. However, the delivery of such plans are also subject to health and safety legislation, designed to protect care workers and clients from risks to their health and safety. The relevant legislation includes:

- General:
  - ○ Health and Safety at Work etc Act 1974;
  - ○ Management of Health and Safety at Work Regulations 1999;
  - ○ Safety Representatives and Safety Committees Regulations 1977;
  - ○ Health and Safety (Consultation with Employees) Regulations 1996.
- Manual handling:
  - ○ Manual Handling Operations Regulations 1992.
- Lifting Equipment:
  - ○ Provision and Use of Work Equipment Regulations 1992 and 1998;
  - ○ Lifting Operations and Lifting Equipment Regulations 1998.

A brief summary of the relevant duties in each is given below. See Appendix 2 for more detailed guidance on specific legislation.

General

Health and Safety at Work etc Act 1974

2 This applies to all work activities. It requires employers to ensure, so far as is reasonably practicable, the health, safety and welfare of all their employees. In particular, employers are required:

- to use 'systems of work' that are 'safe and without risks to health';
- to make arrangements for ensuring safety and the absence of risks to health in connection with the '...use, handling, storage and transport of articles'; and
- to conduct business in such a way as to ensure that others (ie non-employees and members of the public) are not exposed to risks to their health or safety.

These general provisions in the Act are reinforced by Regulations which define in more detail what duty holders must do in particular areas.

Management of Health and Safety at Work Regulations 1999 (MHSW)

3 MHSW are the main health and safety regulations which apply to everyone at work. These cover the general management of health and safety issues. They require all employers to plan, control, organise, monitor and review their work procedures, including:

- assessing the risks, arising from their work, to the health and safety of their employees (including new or expectant mothers and young people) and of anyone else who may be affected;
- recording any significant findings (in

firms with five or more employees);

- implementing preventive and protective measures and ensuring they are properly managed;
- providing employees with adequate information on the health and safety arrangements and the training they need to deal with the risks; and
- co-operating in health and safety matters where others share the workplace.

Self-employed people are similarly required to assess risks, take preventive or protective measures, and co-operate on health and safety matters.

Safety Representatives and Safety Committees Regulations 1977

4   The Safety Representatives and Safety Committees Regulations 1977 provide for trade unions recognised in the workplace to appoint safety representatives. The Regulations set out the functions of representatives and place obligations on employers to enable the representatives to carry out their functions. In particular, employers must:

- consult appointed safety representatives

on health and safety matters; and

- allow representatives time off with pay during working hours to undertake necessary training and to carry out their functions.

Health and Safety (Consultation with Employees) Regulations 1996

5   In workplaces where there are no trade union safety representatives appointed under the 1977 Regulations, the Health and Safety (Consultation with Employees) Regulations 1996 require employers to consult their employees on health and safety matters. Consultation can be direct or via representatives elected by the employees. In the latter case, employers have to make arrangements for the election of representatives from amongst the employees, and the process must be independent and not subject to influence by the employer or management. Representatives elected in accordance with the 1996 Regulations have a narrower range of functions than safety representatives appointed under the 1977 Regulations, but are covered by similar provisions on time off with pay and training.

Manual handling

Manual Handling Operations Regulations 1992

6   Where a risk assessment under regulation 3 of MHSW (see above) shows that there is a risk from manual handling activities, the Manual Handling Operations Regulations

1992 will apply. These are designed specifically to eliminate the manual handling risk or, if this is not possible, to reduce it to acceptable levels. Where work activities include manual handling, employers must:

- avoid the manual handling operation so

far as is reasonably practicable;

- where it cannot be avoided, make a suitable and sufficient risk assessment, taking account of the characteristics of the load (including where this is a person), the task, the working environment, and the physical capabilities of the individuals involved, and any other relevant factors;

- take appropriate steps to reduce the risk to health to the lowest level reasonably practicable.

7 In addition, employers must:

- provide employees with a general indication (and precise information, where it is reasonably practicable to do so) of the weight of each load; and

- review assessments when there is reason to suspect they are no longer valid or there has been a significant change in the manual handling operations.

Lifting equipment

Provision and Use of Work Equipment Regulations (PUWER) 1998

8 PUWER applies to any equipment which is used by an employee at work, from small hand tools to patient hoists and fork lift trucks. In general terms, the Regulations require employers to ensure that equipment provided for use at work is:

- suitable for the intended use and for conditions in which it is used;

- safe for use, maintained in a safe condition and, in certain circumstances, inspected so that it continues to be safe;

- used only by people who have received adequate information, instruction and training; and

- accompanied by suitable safety measures, eg protective devices, markings, warnings.

9 Where the risk assessment under regulation 3 of MHSW (see above) has identified a significant risk to the operator or

other workers from the installation or use of work equipment, the equipment should be inspected by a competent person:

- at suitable intervals;

- each time that exceptional circumstances which are liable to jeopardise the safety of the equipment occur (eg serious damage, major modifications, etc).

10 If the safety of the equipment depends on the installation conditions, it should also be inspected after installation and before being put into service for the first time or after assembly at a new site or new location.

Lifting Operations and Lifting Equipment Regulations (LOLER) 1998

11 LOLER have specific requirements relating to work equipment which is used for lifting and lowering people or loads. This includes any attachments used to anchor, fix or support the lifting equipment and lifting accessories such as chains, slings, eyebolts, etc. They apply to equipment provided for use by people at work and this has implications for maintenance responsibilities in the home care situation. See section on the supply and use of assistive devices.

12 The Regulations require the employer to ensure that lifting equipment is:

● sufficiently strong, stable and suitable for the proposed use;

● positioned or installed to prevent the risk of injury, eg from the equipment or the load falling or striking people;

● visibly marked with any appropriate information, eg the safe working load.

Accessories such as slings and chains should also be marked with this information.

13 Additionally, the employer must ensure that:

● lifting operations are planned, supervised and carried out in a safe manner by competent people;

● lifting equipment used for lifting people is marked accordingly and safe for such a purpose;

● lifting equipment is thoroughly examined by a competent person, where appropriate, and a report of the examination submitted by the competent person to the employer; and

● lifting equipment is thoroughly re-examined if it is exposed to conditions (including wear and tear) which may cause deterioration and result in dangerous situations.

14 The intervals for thorough examination of lifting equipment and accessories in use are as follows:

● every six months for lifting equipment for lifting people and lifting accessories;

● every 12 months for lifting equipment used only for lifting loads; or, in either case

● at intervals specified in an examination scheme drawn up by the competent person to undertake the measures needed to comply with the requirements of the Regulations.

15 Lifting equipment should also be thoroughly examined:

● after installation and before being put into use for the first time (this applies to permanently fixed, rather than mobile equipment);

● after assembly and before being put into service at a new site or location;

● following exceptional circumstances which are liable to jeopardise the safety of the lifting equipment.

Reports of thorough examination should be kept for at least two years or until the next thorough examination and should be available for inspection.

Further information

(Priced publications may be available for free loan from the public library.)

General guidance on the Regulations (available from HSE Books)

A guide to the Health and Safety (Consultation with Employees) Regulations 1996. Guidance on Regulations L95 **HSE Books 1996 ISBN 0 7176 1234 1**

Management of health and safety at work. Management of Health and Safety at Work Regulations 1999. Approved Code of Practice and guidance L21 (Second edition) **HSE Books 2000 ISBN 0 7176 2488 9**

Manual handling. Manual Handling Operations Regulations 1992 (as amended). Guidance on Regulations L23 (Third edition) **HSE Books 2004 ISBN 0 7176 2823 X**

Safe use of lifting equipment. Lifting Operations and Lifting Equipment Regulations 1998. Approved Code of Practice and guidance L113 **HSE Books 1998 ISBN 0 7176 1628 2**

Safe use of work equipment. Provision and Use of Work Equipment Regulations 1998. Approved Code of Practice and guidance L22 (Second edition) **HSE Books 1998 ISBN 0 7176 1626 6**

Safety representatives and safety committees L87 (Third edition) **HSE Books 1996 ISBN 0 7176 1220 1**

Other guidance on manual handling

Getting to grips with handling problems: Worked examples of assessment and reduction of risk in the health services Guidance **HSE Books 1994 ISBN 0 7176 0622 8**

Getting to grips with manual handling: A short guide Leaflet INDG143(rev2) **HSE Books 2004 (single copy free or priced packs of 15 ISBN 0 7176 2828 0)**

Health and safety in care homes HSG220 **HSE Books 2001 ISBN 0 7176 2082 4**

Manual handling in the health services (Second edition) Guidance **HSE Books 1998 ISBN 0 7176 1248 1**

Manual handling: Solutions you can handle HSG115 **HSE Books 1994 ISBN 0 7176 0693 7**

A pain in your workplace? Ergonomic problems and solutions HSG121 **HSE Books 1994 ISBN 0 7176 0668 6**

Other publications

The guide to the handling of patients: Introducing a safer handling policy (Fourth edition) **National Back Pain Association/Royal College of Nursing 1998 ISBN 09530582 5 5**

Handling people: Equipment, advice and information (Second edition) **Disabled Living Foundation 1994 ISBN 0 901908 64 9**

The Home Care Workers' Handbook: The essential guide to care in the home **UKHCA Ltd 1998 ISBN 0 9534243 0 8**

Safer handling of people in the community **BackCare 1999 ISBN 0 1530582 7 1**

Helplines

HSE Infoline
Tel: 08701 545500
(8.30 am to 5.00 pm Monday to Friday)

NHS Direct
Tel: 0845 4647

Support groups

BackCare
16 Elmtree Road, Teddington TW11 8ST
Tel: 020 8977 5474

Useful websites

Health and Safety Executive
www.hse.gov.uk

BackCare
www.backcare.org.uk

Chartered Society of Physiotherapy
www.csp.org.uk

General Osteopathic Council
www.osteopathy.org.uk

British Chiropractic Association
www.chiropractic-uk.co.uk

College of Occupational Therapists
www.cot.co.uk

Appendix 3
Glossary

Assistive devices

Care equipment, eg aids to assist standing and transferring the client.

Care assessment

An assessment of an individual's needs to identify the care input required to support them in their daily life.

This is normally done before work starts in people's homes.

Care provider

An organisation that implements care to the client via its care workers, in accordance with the commissioning organisation's care assessment.

Care worker

An individual employed to deliver social care to the client (employed by local authority, independent organisation or voluntary organisation).

Carer

A carer is a non-employee, eg family, relatives or friends.

Client

A client is the person that needs the care input.

Commissioning organisation

An organisation that identifies an individual's care needs via assessment and purchases the required care provision from a suitable care provider.

Appointed to perform care needs and to purchase care.

Competent person

Someone with sufficient training experience and knowledge to undertake a particular task.

Emergency

A sudden state of danger that will normally require immediate action.

Gantry hoist

A gantry hoist consists of two floor-mounted support frames which are situated on either side of the bed. Two track rails run over the bed and have two motors to which the sling is attached. The sling bar can be lowered and raised to lift an individual off the bed to wash them or change the sheets.

Generic risk assessment

An assessment that encompasses a number of related operations which have similar characteristics.

Hazard

Anything that can cause harm (eg chemicals, electricity, lifting, etc).

Health and safety risk assessment

An assessment of risks arising from specific tasks, work and environment. The purpose being to identify suitable methods to reduce risks so far as is reasonably practicable.

Hoist

A hoist is an aid used to lift clients who are non-weight-bearing.

Individual risk assessment

An assessment of the risks arising specifically from the provision of care to the client. The risk assessment looking at the health and safety of the client and care worker.

Manual handling

Any transporting or supporting of a load (including the lifting, putting down, pushing, pulling, carrying or moving thereof) by hand or bodily force.

Mattress variator

Designed to independently fit on ordinary beds, under the mattress, to help the client to sit up.

Mobility assistance

The use of aids and systems of work to assist client mobility.

Quadrapod

Walking aid, usually a metal stick with a padded rubber handle that has four prongs with ferrules at the bottom, rather than just one, as an ordinary stick has.

Risk

The chance, high or low, that somebody will be harmed by the hazard.

Rotunda

A rotating disc that assists the carer when transfering a client from one surface to another, ie bed to chair.

Tracking hoist

A tracking hoist consists of two parallel tracks fitted to both sides of the room with a moving section running between them.

Transfer board (angled)

This is a device used to assist the carer when sliding a person from one level surface to another, ie wheelchair to commode etc.

Work equipment

Equipment provided by the employer to carry out the task.

Zimmer

A frame used to support a standing client and enable them to walk with independence.

Acknowledgements

The Health and Safety Executive acknowledges the generosity of the following organisations who supplied original information for case studies to help compile this publication:

Andrew Spence/West Suffolk College

Aylesbury Vale Community Healthcare NHS Trust

Bedford Hospital Trust

Cambridgeshire Social Services, Training Section

Care for the Carers Ltd

Cheviots Childrens Centre

Community Occupational Therapy Service, Greenwich Social Services

Community Occupational Therapy, Bury, Lancashire

Directorate of Social Care and Health – London Borough of Lewisham

Disability Service, London Borough of Croydon

Dorchester Disability Services Team – Dorset Social Services

Dorset County Council Social Services

Hackney In House Home Care Team - Services for Older People

Hertfordshire County Council – Home Care Service

Home Care Department – Lambeth Social Services

Hounslow Social Services

Jewish Care

Kent Home Care Service

Lewisham Community Occupational Therapy Service

Lincolnshire Social Services

London Borough of Enfield – Social Services Group

London Borough of Harrow Social Services

London Borough of Hillingdon Social Services Department

London Borough of Newham, Home Support Service

London Borough of Sutton

Motability

South Buckinghamshire NHS Trust

Suffolk Social Services

WHCS – Wandsworth Home Care Service

Questionnaire

Handling home care:

Achieving safe, efficient and positive outcomes for care workers and clients

This publication was written for care providers and care workers. To help us assess it, please complete and return this questionnaire to the address overleaf. Postage is free.

Are you a:

☐ carer? ☐ care provider? ☐ care user? ☐ care worker?

Did you find the publication:

clear and straightforward? **1 2 3 4** *difficult to understand?*

Was the publication:

well presented? **1 2 3 4** *poorly presented?*

Was the publication useful to you in identifying the health and safety risks associated with what you do?

very useful **1 2 3 4** *not useful*

Was the advice in the publication useful to you in identifying ways of controlling health and safety risks?

very useful **1 2 3 4** *not useful*

Did the publication help you to understand your responsibilities for health and safety:

☐ *very well* ☐ *well* ☐ *a little* ☐ *not at all?*

How much of the advice was relevant?

☐ *all* ☐ *most* ☐ *some* ☐ *none*

What additional information would you like to have seen in the publication?

continued over...

Thank you for taking the time to answer these questions

additional information continued...

Thank you for taking the time to answer these questions

FIRST FOLD

HC

SECOND FOLD

THIRD FOLD

Tuck A into B to form envelope
Please do not staple or glue

A

B

Printed and published by the Health and Safety Executive   6/04   C70